FUN AND LEARN
JUMBO
500
MATH ACTIVITIES

14 12

20 6
2
4 10

2 4 5

MANOJ PUBLICATIONS

Tick the sets that have the same number of fruits.

  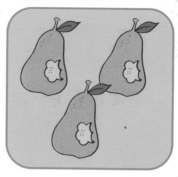 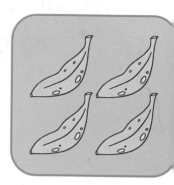

Count and write how many pieces of each object are there in the picture.

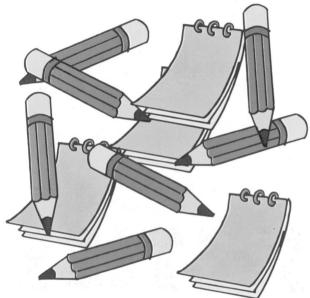

Pencil [ ]

Notebook [ ]

Encircle the hidden numbers 1-5 in the picture given below.

Find the answers quickly.

7	+	5	=	
+		+		+
1	+	4	=	
=		=		=
	+		=	17

Look at the numbers and fill up the blanks.

1 2 3 4 5 6 7 8 9 10

Which number :

a. comes after 4? _____

b comes before 5? _____

2

Count and write the number of stars on each flag.

Count and write the number of petals and leaves.
Remember each flower has five petals. Fill in the circles.

◯ **Petals +** ◯ **Leaves =** ☐

Number the picture pieces in the correct order.

1

Look at the two sets of animals below.

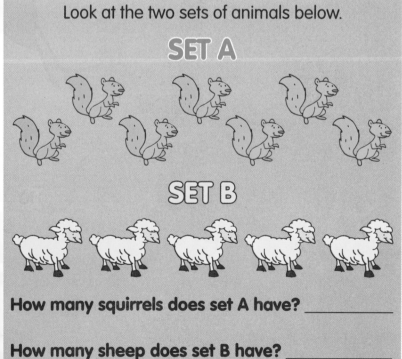

SET A

SET B

How many squirrels does set A have? _____

How many sheep does set B have? _____

Write the numbers that comes between the given numbers.

85		87
30		32
43		45

25		27
15		17
24		26

Write the missing numbers.

3	4	9
4	8	
1	2	3
6	10	15

Solve the sums in the grid by filling in the missing numbers.

```
      2
      +
6  -  2  =  
      =
6  +     =  10
```

Write the numbers that come after 5 and after 9.

5 ___ 9 ___

Complete the sums using the codes.

Fish = 4   Parrot = 7   Bee = 5

Fish + Parrot = ☐

Bee − Fish = ☐

Parrot + Parrot = ☐

Parrot + Bee = ☐

Count the number of objects.

○

Cross out the following as directed.

Fourth cheese form the left

 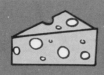 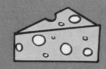  

Sixth chair form the left

Solve the math puzzle.

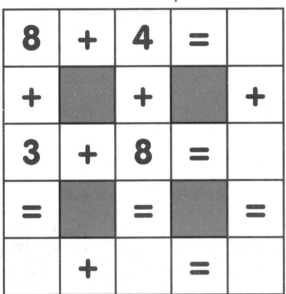

Solve the sums and write the answers.

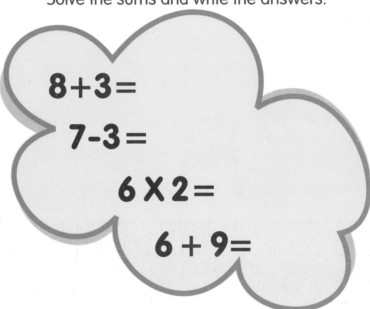

$8+3=$

$7-3=$

$6 \times 2=$

$6+9=$

Colour each domino that has equal sets.

How many mice are there?

There are _____ mice.

5

Colour the fish which has the biggest number.

Write the number that comes between the given numbers.

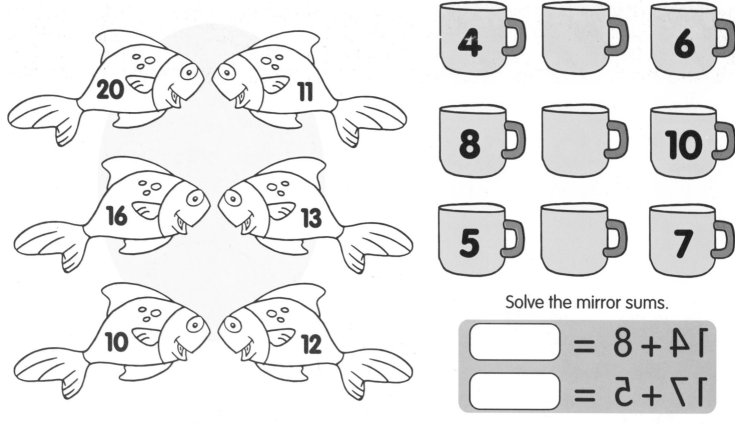

Solve the mirror sums.

$$14 + 8 = \boxed{}$$

$$17 + 5 = \boxed{}$$

Match the sums to the answers.

Draw a line to match the answers to their digits.

 4 x 1

 6 x 2

 5 x 3

 2 x 5

 4 x 2

How many carrots are there?

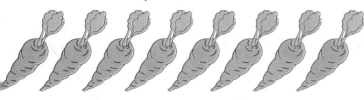

There are _____ carrots.

Colour the stars according to the number of gloves.

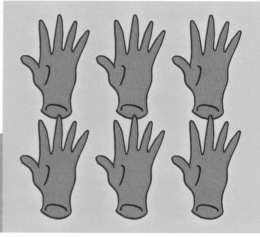

Solve the sums using the clues.
Write the answers in the blank boxes.

parrot =2   banana =9   mobile phone =5

Count and write how many turnips are there.

 **+** 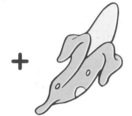 **=** ▢

 **×**  **=** ▢

 **—**  **=** ▢

_____

Match the pictures with the numbers.

   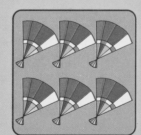      

4 ◀—— **1** —— **3** —— **6** ——▶

Match pairs of numbers that come together.

 50  7  15  10  46

45   16   11   8   51

Count the number of objects.

Follow the table of 8 and join the stars.

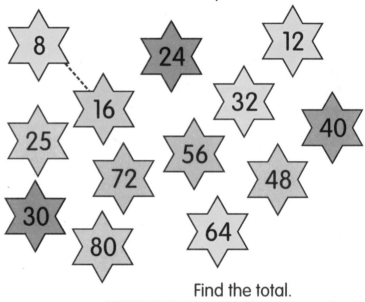

Find the total.

Colour the pictures that have even numbers.

7   6   3

2   4   1

Follow the codes and colour the pictures.

4 = ●   6 = ●   5 = ○   3 = ●   2 = ●   7 = ●

Egg characters: 2+4   10-7   5+2   2×2   9-7   6-1

Solve the problem and write the answer in the circle.

$$10-4=\bigcirc$$

Join the dots from 1-15.
Colour the picture brightly.

Count and tick the total number of the pictures.

⑨   ⑩   ⑫   ⑬

⑩   ⑪   ⑦   ⑨

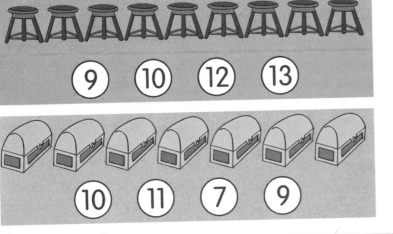

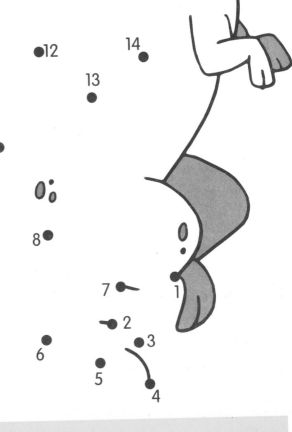

Colour the numbers which are not in order.

| 1 | 2 | 3 | 5 | 4 | 6 | 7 | 8 | 9 | 10 |

Colour the given number of objects.

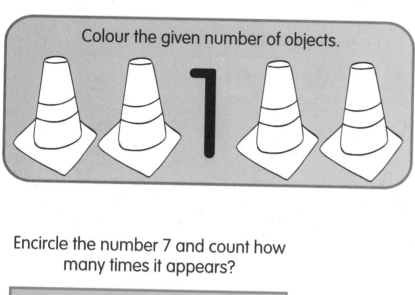

1

There are 6 tomatoes. Add 4 more tomatoes to the group. Draw and complete the sum.

$6 + \underline{\quad} = \boxed{}$

Encircle the number 7 and count how many times it appears?

7 5 5 2 3 4 3
  7 5 3 2 5
  5 4 2 7 7
2   3 3 5
          4 2 2
          3 3
        3 7
    4   4
      7 3
    3 7
    7   7
      7 4
  3 7 7
        3
  7 7
7 3 7

Add 3 to the numbers on each tree, and then match the answer with the apples.

6 8 5 7 9 2

3   4

Colour the third, fifth, seventh and tenth star.

Colour the second, fifth and eighth circle.

10

Join up equal values. One has been done for you.

Ones/Tens	Written form	Expanded	Number
10 1 1 / 1 1 1	1 ten + 6 ones	10+3	20
10 1 / 1 1	2 ten + 0 ones	10+5	11
10 1 1 1 / 1 1 1	1 ten + 5 ones	10+1	13
10 10	1 ten + 1 ones	10+6	15
10 1	1 ten + 3 ones	10+10	16

Solve the sums.

7	+	5	=	
+		+		+
3	+	10	=	
=		=		=
	+		=	25

Follow the table of 3 to help the dog reach the house.

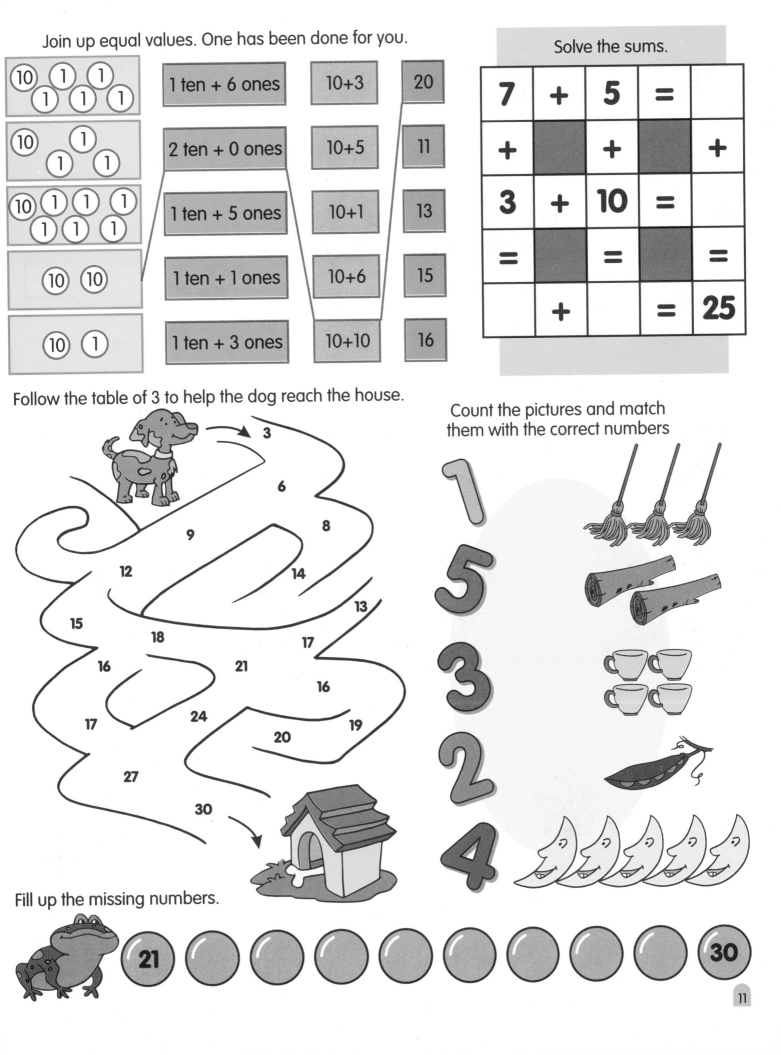

3
6
9
8
12
14
15
13
18
17
16
21
16
17
24
19
20
27
30

Count the pictures and match them with the correct numbers

1
5
3
2
4

Fill up the missing numbers.

21 ◯ ◯ ◯ ◯ ◯ ◯ ◯ ◯ 30

Write the numbers that comes before the given numbers.

(15)

(20)

(8)

(13)

(23)

(27)

Place the numbers correctly.

___ + ___ + ___ + = 6

___ + ___ + ___ + = 7

___ + ___ + ___ + = 8

___ + ___ + ___ + = 9

___ + ___ + ___ + = 10

___ + ___ + ___ + = 11

Find the answers.

20 +14	10 +12	15 +14	18 +17

How many sides does each figure have?

ⓐ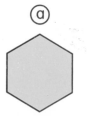

ⓑ

ⓒ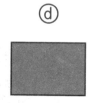

ⓓ

_____ sides

_____ sides

_____ sides

_____ sides

Count and tick the correct number.

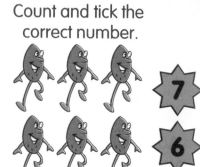

What's missing? Write the correct number in each box.

1 2 1 [ ] [ ] 2 1 2

12

Match them with correct tree sums.

ⓐ   ⓑ   ⓒ

 10-7    2×3    3+1

Let's enhance our maths skills by solving your problems.

a. $7 \times 2 =$ d. $18 + 1 =$

b. $5 \times 3 =$ e. $10 - 5 =$

c. $7 + 3 =$ f. $16 \div 2 =$

a. [ ]   d. [ ]

b. [ ]   e. [ ]

c. [ ]   f. [ ]

Add and subtract numbers in such a way that the solution comes to 20.

6 + ___   25 - ___   15 + ___   30 - ___   20

Match the pictures with the yellow number circles in the centre.

 ④   ①   10

 ⑧   ②   6

  ③

 ⑤   ④   2

  ⑤

  ⑥

 ⑦   ⑦   1

  ⑧

 ③   ⑨   9

  ⑩

Find the numbers and then colour them in different shades.

13

Encircle the group of 3 pictures.

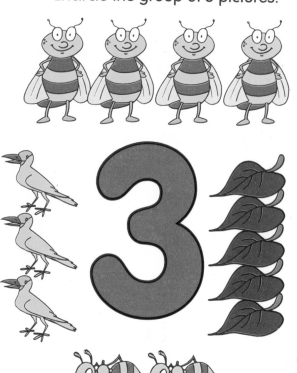

Draw lines to connect numbers with their matching sets.

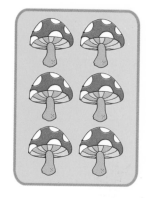

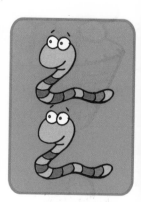

Identify the number pattern and fill up the missing numbers to complete the sequence.

1   3   5

Solve the sum.

$12 + 5 - 2 =$ ◯

Skip in 5s and help the bee find the hive.

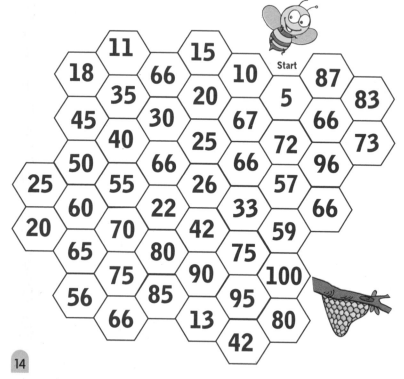

Write '–' and '=' between the numbers to show subtraction facts, and then, encircle the facts. The facts can be found by moving across or down. Two have been done for you.

15	5	6	10	4	9	8	3
4	3	2	7	2	11	6	5
12 – 4 = 8		3	2	7	4	9
2	4	1	15	8	7	6	2
7	6	14	5	9	4	8	0
1	14	2	9	6	3	2	16
0	7	9	3	0	9	6	8
12	7	5	10	6	4	1	8

14

Encircle the basket that has two flowers.

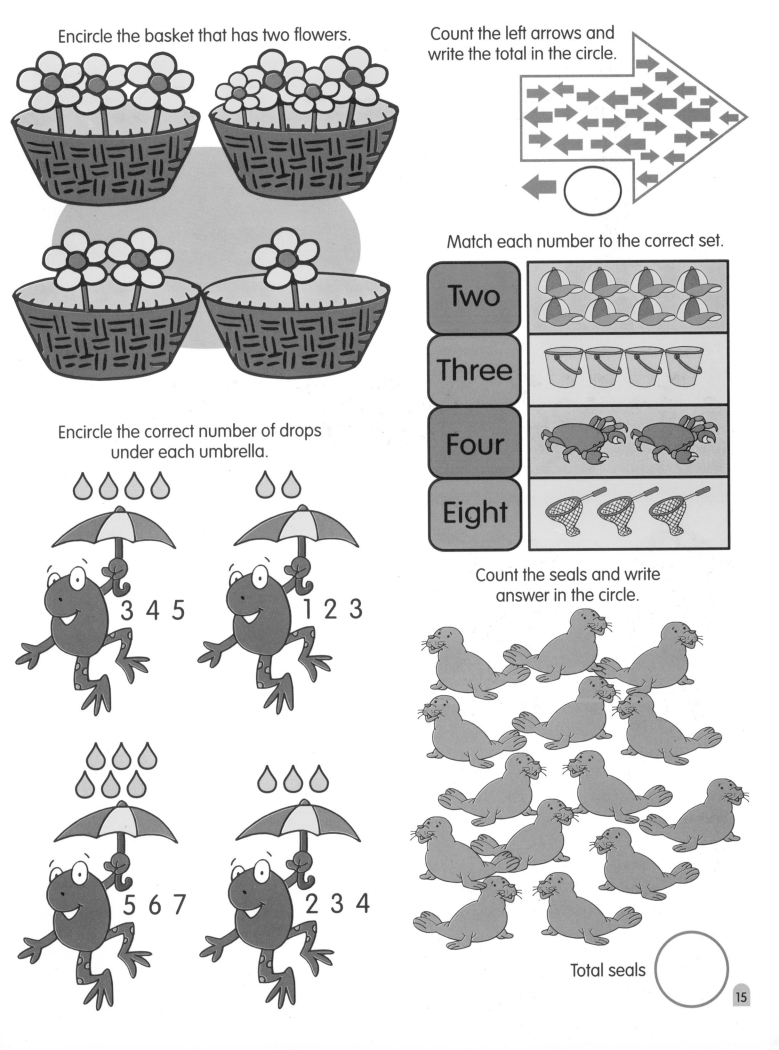

Count the left arrows and write the total in the circle.

Match each number to the correct set.

Two

Three

Four

Eight

Encircle the correct number of drops under each umbrella.

3 4 5

1 2 3

5 6 7

2 3 4

Count the seals and write answer in the circle.

Total seals

Colour the pictures as per given numbers.

1 2 3

3

2

1

Count, subtract and write the answer.

Tick the book which has maximum number.

13 20
17 15

Colour the odd numbers.

9 8 7
1 5 7
2 4 3

Colour any two circles to make five.

2
0 1

0 1
3 4

Count each group of objects and draw a line to match the number names.

Five

Three

Six

Four

Ten

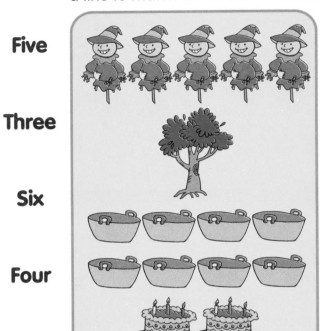

One

Eight

Two

Nine

Seven

15 + 10

20 + 8

10 + 7

20 + 5

Count the objects and encircle the correct number.

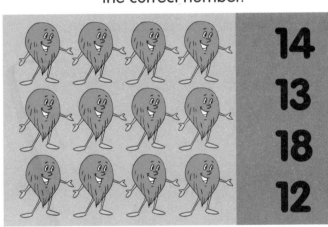

14

13

18

12

Fill up the answers.

$5 \times 5 =$ ☐

$2 \times 5 =$ ☐

$4 \times 4 =$ ☐

$7 \times 8 =$ ☐

$7 \times 2 =$ ☐

Write three different addition equations for the sums.

20

__ + __ = 20

__ + __ = 20

__ + __ = 20

10

__ + __ = 10

__ + __ = 10

__ + __ = 10

Calculate the sums, and then colour all the even numbers with yellow and odd with green.

4 + 5

5 + 7

5 + 2

Subtract 2 from the numbers and help the plane reach the last cloud.

-4 -2 -2 -2 -2 -2

20 16

Fill up the gird correctly.

5	+	6	=	
+		+		+
6	+	5	=	
=		=		=
	+		=	22

Join the numbers in order.

1	2	6
5	3	4
3	6	5
2	7	11
7	8	3
4	9	
9	10	

Solve the sums.

7 − 3 =

8 ÷ 2 =

18

Help the frog reach the pond by following the trail of even numbers.

52	69	21	33	43	51
18	23	28	20	18	15
7	8	11	27	40	55
83	47	12	13	70	63
9	2	87	49	39	4
10	61	72	26	91	68
87	42	83	31	56	22
93	77	53	81	97	90

Find the greatest and the smallest number in each set.

Greatest ☐

Smallest ☐

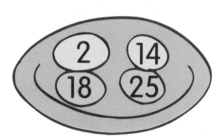

Greatest ☐

Smallest ☐

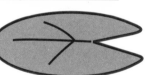

Count and write the correct number of carrots.

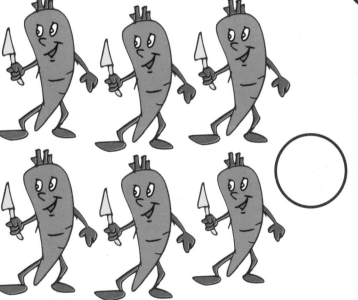

◯

Colour the given numbers as directed.

1-5 = pink	6-10 = yellow	11-15 = green

Colour the right number of pictures.

4 — 🌂🌂🌂🌂🌂🌂   2 — 🧦🧦🧦

19

Count the pictures. Then, tick in the correct circle to show whether the number is even or odd.

even	odd
○	○
○	○
○	○
○	○
○	○

Join the numbers and colour it.

Encirlce the number 3s.

| 3 | 4 | 3 | 1 | 3 | 5 | 3 | 3 | 7 |

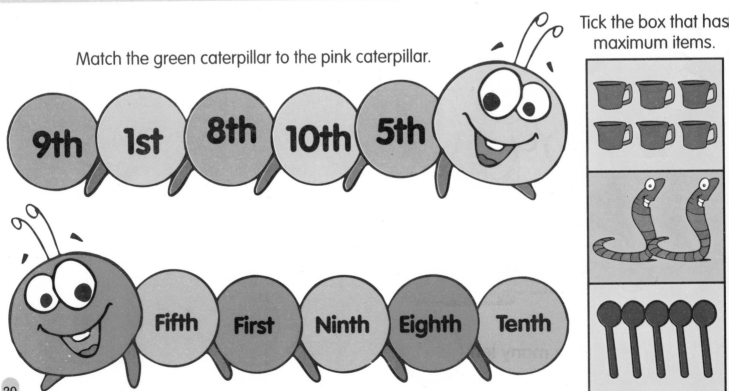

Match the green caterpillar to the pink caterpillar.

9th 1st 8th 10th 5th

Fifth First Ninth Eighth Tenth

Tick the box that has maximum items.

Encircle the third and fifth picture in the row.

Which is third from the left _____

Which is sixth from the right _____

Encircle the correct dice.

Follow the number pattern and write the missing numbers.

3 4 5 3 4 5 ☐ ☐ 5

How many apples are there on the tree?

How many left ◯

Solve the number puzzle.

7	+		=	11
+		+		+
1	+		=	10
=		=		=
	+		=	

Fill in the missing numbers.

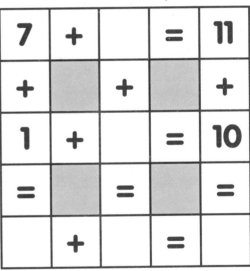

7 + 5 = ◯

4 + ◯ = 8

21

Colour the muffin that belongs to the child in accordance with number.

Match the number so that difference equals the number on the snail.

12		2
10	(9)	1
11		3

9		8
10	(5)	5
13		4

Complete the facts given below.

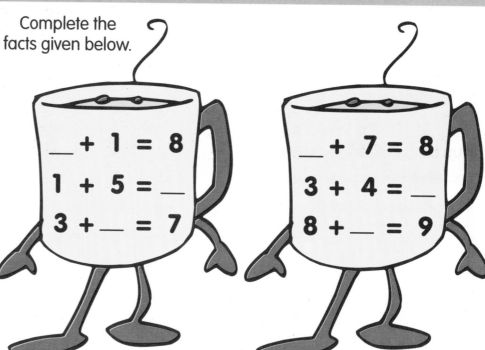

_ + 1 = 8

1 + 5 = _

3 + _ = 7

_ + 7 = 8

3 + 4 = _

8 + _ = 9

Place the numbers accurately.

6   8

Place the missing numbers on the stars.

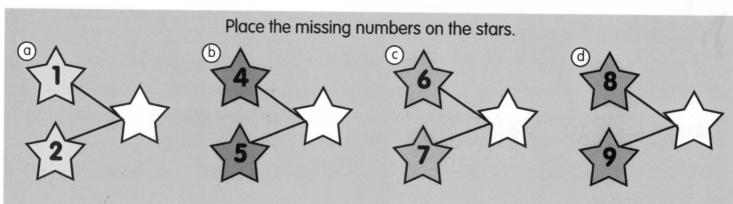

a) 1 2

b) 4 5

c) 6 7

d) 8 9

22

Write the numbers that add up to the sum shown in the squares.

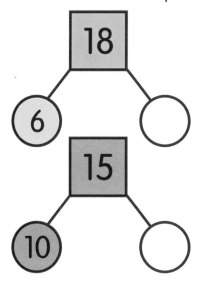

Find the answers.

16 - 6 =

12 - 3 =

Count the candles and tick the number.

2 5 3

Fill up the numbers in the squares.

	-	7	=	2
-		-		+
3	+		=	7
=		=		=
	+	3	=	

Fill in the boxes to complete the sums.

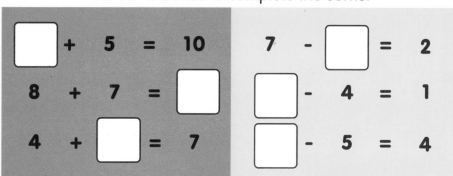

☐ + 5 = 10

8 + 7 = ☐

4 + ☐ = 7

7 - ☐ = 2

☐ - 4 = 1

☐ - 5 = 4

Join the questions whose sum is 10 and help the boy reach the treasure box.

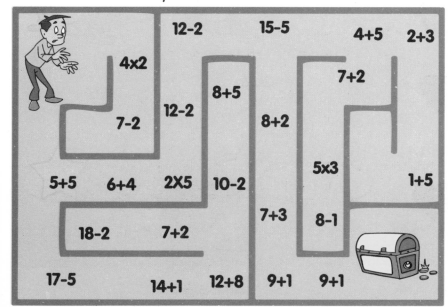

12-2   15-5   4+5   2+3
4x2
8+5   7+2
12-2
7-2   8+2
5+5   6+4   2X5   10-2   5x3   1+5
18-2   7+2   7+3   8-1
17-5   14+1   12+8   9+1   9+1

Colour the correct answer for each problem and write it in the blanks.

6 x 4 = _____   3 + 9 = _____

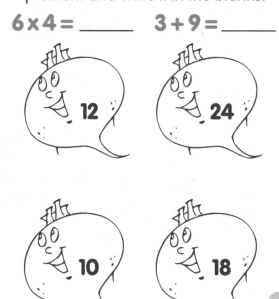

12   24

10   18

23

Write the missing numbers on the bells.
The sum of two bells should be 50.

50

35 + ____

____ + 20

Colour the odd number balloons
red and even numbers yellow.

1

4

3   5

7

10   8

9

Connect the numbers and find the picture.

12

15

6   9

3

45

42

39   33

36

18

21

24

30

27

Count and write the answers.

Small hearts ( )   **Big hearts** ( )

Colour the equation whose answer is 30.

15+5

15+10   **30**   15+0

15+15

Use your brain to solve the picture sums.

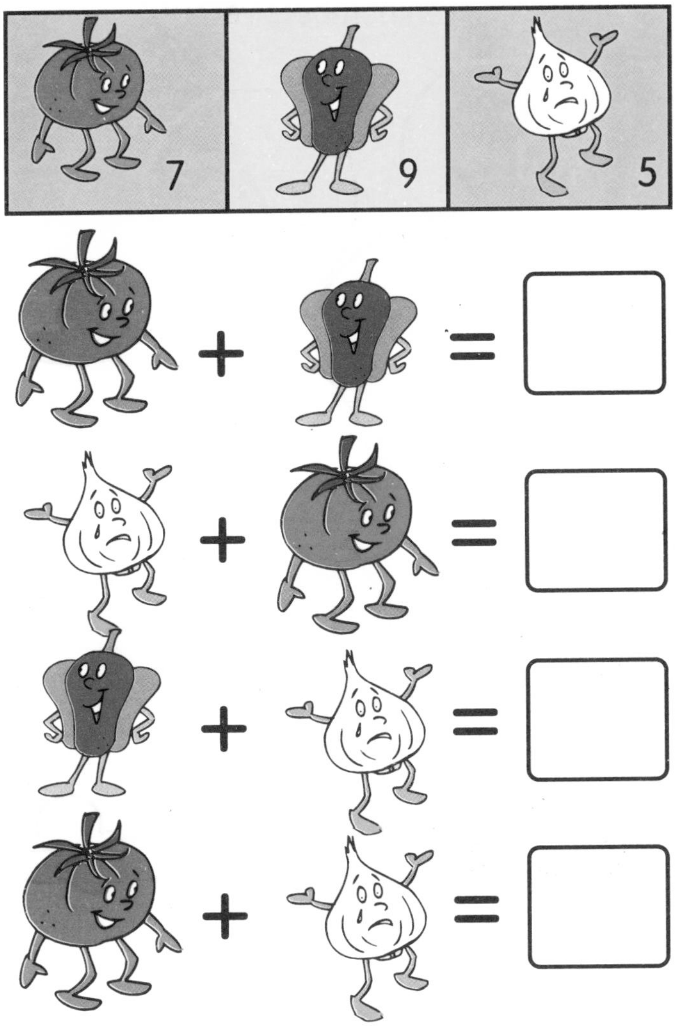

🍅 7	🫑 9	🧅 5

🍅 + 🫑 = ☐

🧅 + 🍅 = ☐

🫑 + 🧅 = ☐

🍅 + 🧅 = ☐

Calculate the total.

🌽 **+** 🌽 **=** ◯

Count the number of sheep.

How many apples are there in the box?
Add 2 and write the answer.

Apple ◯ **+2 =** ◯

Write the missing numbers.

| 11 | 12 | | 14 | |
| 16 | | 18 | | 20 |

Count the hats.

🎩 = ◯   🎩 = ◯   🎩 = ◯

25

Which number is the most repeated
on the flower. Tick all of them.

Write numbers that come before and after the
given number on the wings of the butterfly.

Find the solution.

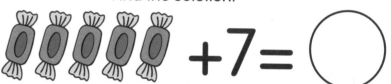

+7 = ◯

Colour the first, fourth, and seventh toucan.

Match the correct number of bats to their balls.

How many tools are there?

Fill up the missing numbers.

1. Numbers after:	45, __	22, __	55, __	65, __
2. Numbers before:	__, 12	__, 18	__, 25	__, 40

How many fruits are walking? Encircle the correct answer.

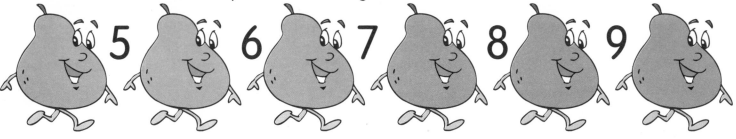

5   6   7   8   9

Count the flowers and tick the right answer.

24-15   16-8

30-10   18-4

Solve the sums.

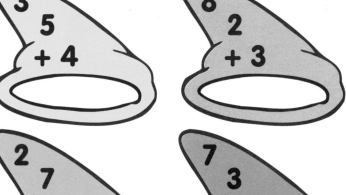

3
5
+ 4

8
2
+ 3

2
7
+ 3

7
3
+ 9

Match the numbers so that their difference equals the number in the star.

12   2

10   9   1

11   3

27

This is a number pattern of reverse counting.

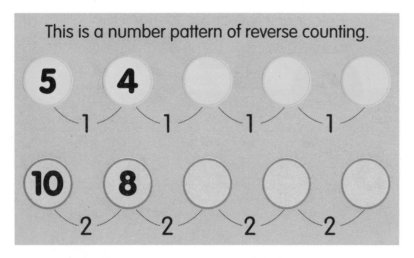

5   **4**   ◯   ◯   ◯
   1   1   1   1

10   **8**   ◯   ◯   ◯
    2   2   2   2

Colour any two watermelons to make 13.

Help duck reach home safely by writing the missing numbers. It should take steps in 2s.

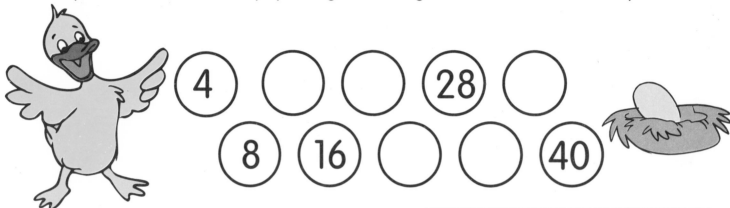

4   ◯   ◯   28   ◯

8   16   ◯   ◯   40

There are 5 tortoises , 3 more tortoises join the group. Draw and complete the sum.

5 + ___ = ☐

Match the numbers on the dogs with the answers on the bones.

7+8

4+8

17

5+4

15

14+8

14 + 3

5 + 6

Find the greatest and the smallest number in each set.

25　20　15

Greatest ▢

Smallest ▢

8　17　25

Greatest ▢

Smallest ▢

Colour any two circles to make five.

2　0　1

2　8　3　7

Tick the coins with the correct answers.

14　16　15

8+8

13　20　19

9+4

7　8　9

7+2

18　19　20

15+5

Count, subtract and write the answer.

10 - 4 = ◯

Calculate the sums, and then colour all the even numbers blue and odd with red.

0 + 3

3 + 2

3 + 3

2 + 0

Write the number after and before.

16

10

21

17

Solve the following equation.

	+	6	=	18
+		+		+
20	+	12	=	
=		=		=
	+		=	

Which set matches with the number?

Cross out the extra pencils so that they match with the correct number given.

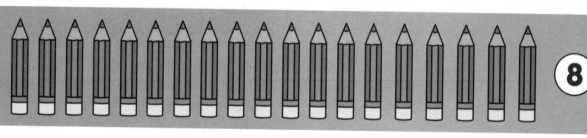

8

Complete the number patterns.

2, 2, 5, 7, 4, 3, _ _ _ _ _

6, 6, 1, 2, 3, 6, _ _ _ _ _

Multiply and find the answer.

10 x 5 = ◯

2 x 5 = ◯

5 x 4 = ◯

Count the animals and birds in the picture.

Solve the problems and match each question to the correct answer balloon. Colour according to the questions.

7 6 9 4

3 8

8-2   2+1   3+4

4+5   2+2   12-4

There are 5 cheese. If 2 are eaten how many are left?

Fill up the circle with correct number.

$+\bigcirc = 12$

Draw the missing number from 1-5.

5 3 1 2

Calculate the answers and colour each part according to the number codes.

5+1
6+1
9-2
3+3
6+1
3+4
12-6
8-2
10-4
2x3
6+1
10-3
11-4

6 = ⬤

7 = ⬤

31

Count how many objects are there in each set and then count how many are there altogether.

Altogether : _____

32

Colour the picture as per given number.

5

Solve the addition sum by adding the small cirlces.

+   =

Count the number of objects. Then colour the boxes with the sum having the same answer.

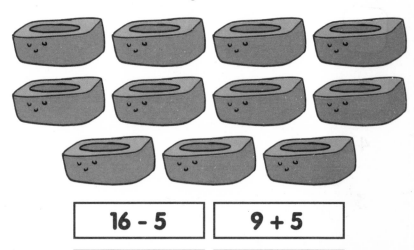

| 16 - 5 | 9 + 5 |
| 11 - 2 | 8 + 4 |

Match the digits to the answers..

4	3	1
9	7	2
5	0	6

10 - 5	10 - 10	10 - 8
10 - 1	10 - 4	10 - 6

Fill up the missing blanks to get the answers written on the fish.

17

9 + _____

23

15 + _____

Determine the answer of the problem.

7 + 8 − 9 =

Solve the addition sums and match the answers with the numbers given.

1	2	3	4	5

☐ + 2 = 5

2 + ☐ = 4

4 + ☐ = 9

3 + ☐ = 7

5 + ☐ = 6

Solve the sum.
Colour the balls to match the answer.

25-17=

Complete the sums.

_____ − 2 = 3

_____ − 4 = 14

33

Two digits should add up to 20.
Calculate and write the numbers.

20

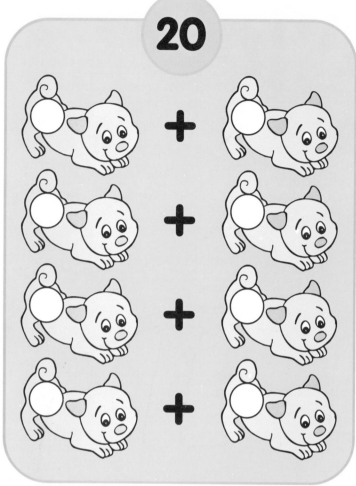

Fill up the missing numbers so that each add up to 10.

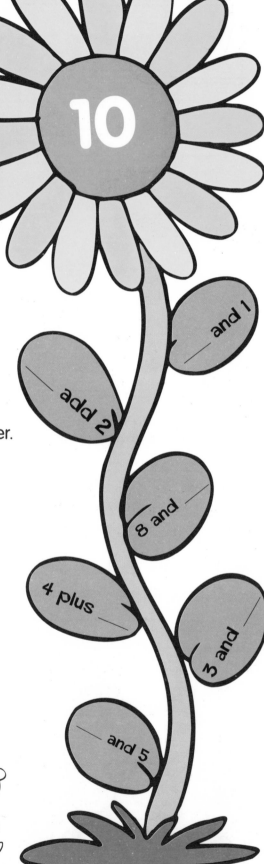

I have ___ flowers. How many more do I need to make 10? Draw the rest flowers.

Find the answer.

$3 \times 2 =$

Tick the correct answer.

Colour any two to make 4.

5
8
9

Solve the sums.

3 X 2 = ...

7 - 3 = ...

2 + 2 = ...

8 - 2 = ...

3 - 2 = ...   2 X 4 = ...

12 - 3 = ...

6 - 2 = ...

Solve and match the correct sum.

7+5 = ◯
6+6 = ◯
2+3 = ◯

Colour the pictures that have odd numbers.

7   6

4   3

Use the number codes to colour.

| 16 = brown | 14 = gray | 12 = green | 15 = blue |

13+2

7+7

17-3

7+7

20-4

12+4

6+6

10+6   9+3

15+1

4+8

17-1

14+2

15-3

11+1   10+5

Solve each sum.

```
  21        07
+ 13      + 40
_____    _____


  57        93
- 35      - 27
_____    _____
```

Fill in the missing numbers with the table of 2.

20   6

2

4   10

35

Match each number to the correct set.

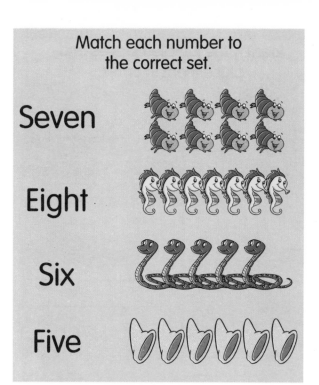

Seven

Eight

Six

Five

Add each row.

6	5
2	5
+ 5	+ 8

18

Total up the number of cheese.
Tick the question whose sum is equal to the number of cheese.

4+5	12-8
5-3	2×3

Write the correct number on the balloons.

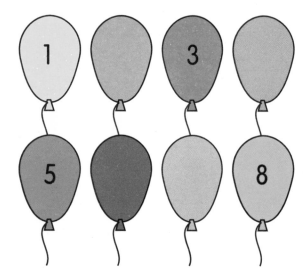

1   3

5   8

Colour the given number of objects.

3

Solve the number puzzle.

3	+	9	=	
+		+		+
1	+	1	=	
=		=		=
	+		=	14

36

Colour the picture. Objects numbered 1-6 should be coloured in blue.

Identify the jumbled pieces and place them in order.

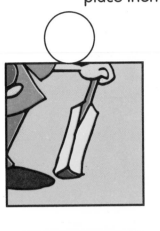 

Encircle the given number of animals and birds in each row.

 2

1

3

Count and tick the correct answer.

7 8 9 10

Write the missing number.

 **2**   **6**

     8

Solve the maths problems.

$$+\begin{array}{r}34\\22\end{array}$$

$$+\begin{array}{r}14\\73\end{array}$$

$$-\begin{array}{r}45\\13\end{array}$$

$$-\begin{array}{r}63\\25\end{array}$$

Count and write the total number of fishes in the picture.

_____

Tick the petals with correct answer.

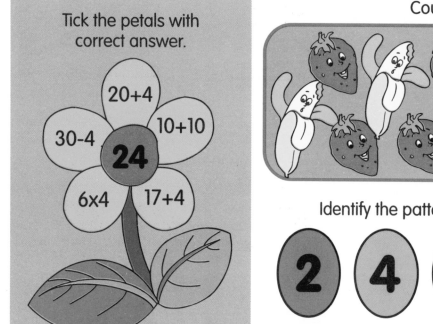

Count and write the total.

Identify the pattern and write the missing numbers.

2   4   ⬭   8   ⬭   12

Encircle the correct number of bones in the bowl.

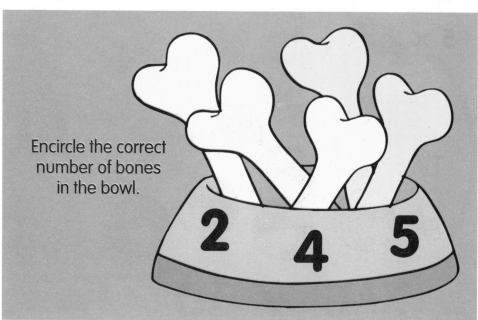

Help John match the correct pairs of dogs.

Count the number of objects in each set.

In each set, count and write the total number of objects. Also write the half of it.

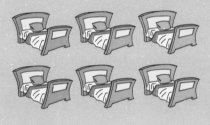

___altogether. Half is ___.

___altogether. Half is ___.

___altogether. Half is ___.

Calculate the sums. Encircle the answers in the box.

$4 + 4 =$
$3 \times 3 =$
$9 \div 3 =$
$5 \times 2 =$
$4 + 3 =$

THREE NINE
SEVEN
TWO
TEN ONE
EIGHT
FIVE

Solve the sums.

$12 \div 3 = \boxed{}$

$10 - 8 = \boxed{}$

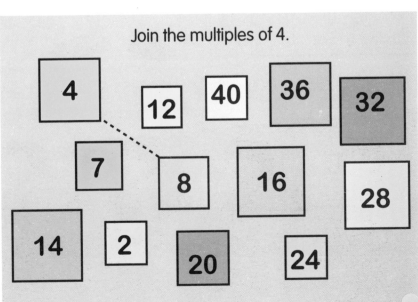

Join the multiples of 4.

4   12   40   36   32
7   8   16   28
14   2   20   24

Rack your brain and solve the maths grid.

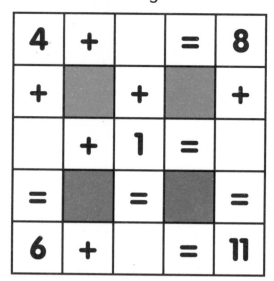

How many objects are there in each box? Encircle the correct number.

4 6   **14 12**

Number the pieces of the puzzle serially.

How many times does the number 5 appear in the circle?

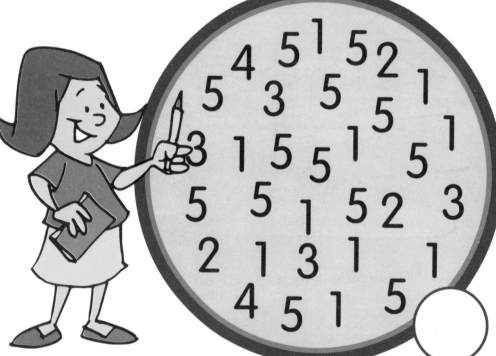

Encircle the number that is equal to the men.

2   4   5   6   7

40

Colour the picture using the number clues.

10 = yellow   20 = pink   25 = green

10-5

10+10

21-1

2×5

26-6

27-2

7+3

5+5

5×4

23+2

6+4

18+2

2×10

28-3

5×5

Add the following.

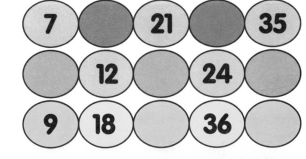

+

=

( )

Fill up the missing numbers in the circles given below.

7		21		35
	12		24	
9	18		36	

Count the objects in each jar.

[   ]

[   ]

Colour the given number of hens.

4

There are two numbers on the dart, encircle the digits that equal to those numbers.

7+4

14+7   **8**   5-2

15-7

11+4

18-2   **12**   15+3

13-1

Count, subtract and write the answer.

15-7=◯

Match the mushrooms with the answers.

2X5

4X4

15

16

4X7

6X5

24

10

3X5

30

8X3

28

Encircle the greater number in each block.

4   8

9   7

Colour the circle with the smallest number.

6   3

7   1

2   8

Tick the set with least stars.

42

Use the key given below to solve the sums.

2	3	4	5	6

Encircle the set with higher number.

Encircle the pictures in each row as given.

Find the answers.

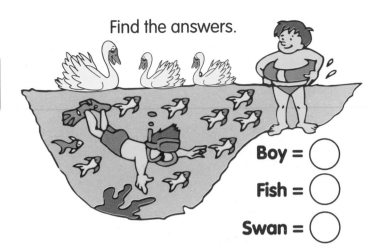

Boy = ◯

Fish = ◯

Swan = ◯

Cross the odd one out in each set.

7 7 7 7 7 7 7

5 5 5 5 5 5 5

Trace the strings to find the respective balls of the boys.

Skip and write the answers.

Say aloud, trace and write.

1	2	3	4	5	6	7	8	9	10
1	2	3	4	5	6	7	8	9	10

Read the clues on the colour palletes and write the numbers.

Count and fill in the table.

Solve the sums.

5×5 _____ $12 \div 4$ _____

4×6 _____

$13 - 7$ _____

$7 + 4$ _____

4×8 _____ $15 \div 3$ _____

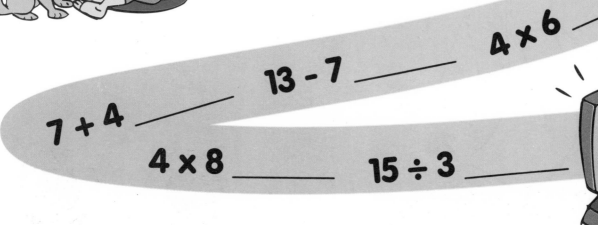

Colour the given number of nurses.

3

Tick the right answer.

18

| 15+8 | 9 X 2 | 14-5 |

Colour the circle with the smallest number.

| 5 | 7 | 2 |
| 3 | 9 | 4 |

Write the numbers from 11 to 20 in correct order.

13

11

12

Guess the number patterns and write down the missing numbers.

49

7

14

28

10

60

30

Match the questions with the answers by drawing a line between them.

⑲ ⑤ ⑰ ⑫

8+4

5+4

18+1

5+9

12+8

4+1

7+3

14+3

Match the fishes to their baits.

15–2 =

23–5 =

30-5 =

29-14 =

13

15

25

18

Cross which one is not in correct order.

⑧ ⑯ ㉕ ㉜ ㊵

Count the flowers and write the answer below.

🌸🌸🌸🌸🌸 **+** 🌸🌸🌸

_____ flowers   _____ flowers   _____ flowers altogether

Count and tick the correct answer.

⑥ ⑧ ⑦

Count and write the answers.

Tatal stars are:_____

Write the missing numbers.

1	2	3		5		7		9	
11		13	14		16	17		19	
	22	23		25		27		29	30
31	32		34		36	37		39	40
41		43			46		48		50

Solve the sums.

2+2 [ ]   10-5 [ ]

Write a number in each circle so that each multiplication problem gets solved.

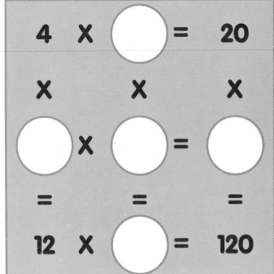

4 × ◯ = 20
× × ×
◯ × ◯ = ◯
= = =
12 × ◯ = 120

Read and write the answer.

★ ★ ★ ★ ★ ★ ★ ★ ★ ★
★ ★ ★ ★   **and one more is** ◯

Solve the sum.

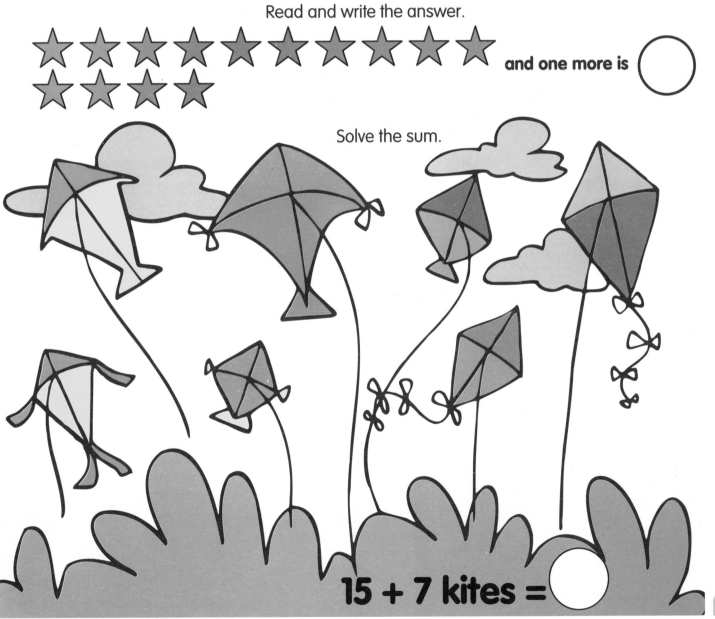

15 + 7 kites = ◯

47

Read the clues on the cup and write the numbers.

4 tens 4 ones   6 tens 1 ones   5 tens 3 ones

Encircle the correct picture in each row.

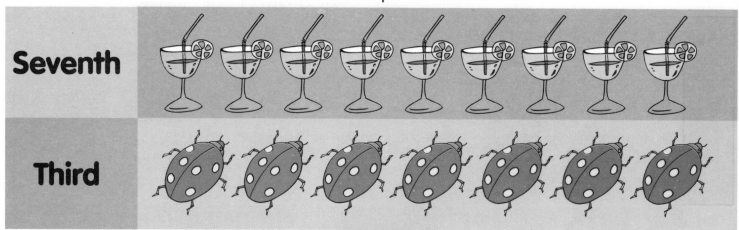

Seventh

Third

Count different types of animals
and write the correct count.

Solve
the sums.

5
×
2
+
◯
=
18

Find the answers.

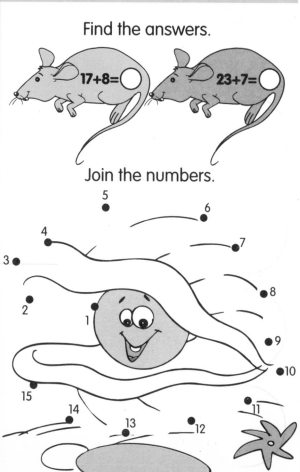

17+8=◯   23+7=◯

Join the numbers.

Write the correct count in each box.

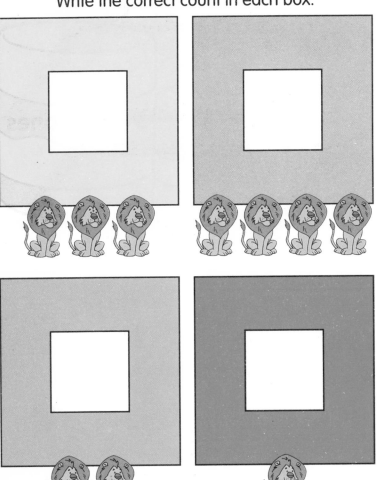

Count the different birds.

Count the objects in each box.

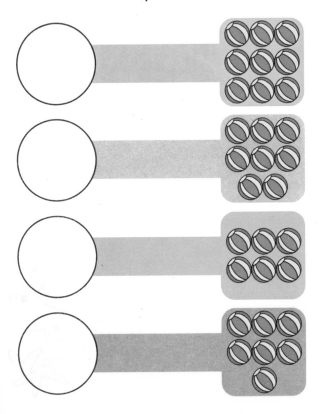

What's missing? Write the correct numbers in the boxes.

Match those that go together.

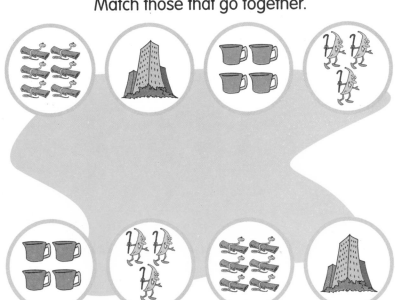

Colour any 5 bears in the set.

Draw the given number of apples in each tray.

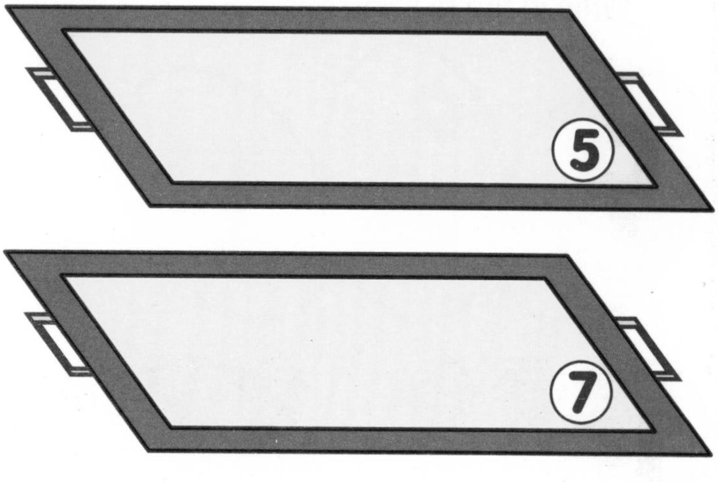

⑤

⑦

Fill up the missing numbers.

13

7

3

1

Trace the number from 1-20

1	2	3	4	5
6	7	8	9	10
11	12	13	14	15
16	17	18	19	20

Join the numbers to find the hidden picture.

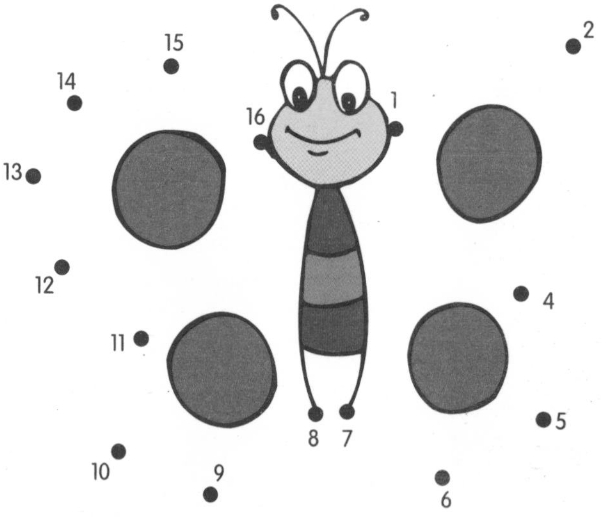

15
14
13
12
11
10
9
16
1
8 7
2
3
4
5
6

Count the dots on each fish.

What comes between?
Write in the missing numbers.

9 __ 11

15 __ 17

Write the correct number on the animals in the bottom picture.

8   5   3   1

Count the fish. Write the count.

Complete the flower vase correctly.

15   20   10
=   +
−   10   +

+   10   =
2

×   24   +
3   =   4

How many tens? How many ones? And how many altogether?

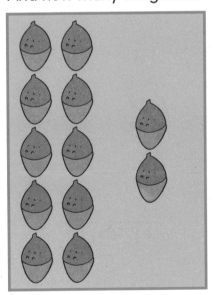

Tens	Ones

= _____

Solve the sum.

5
+ 8
× 2
=
◯

How many?

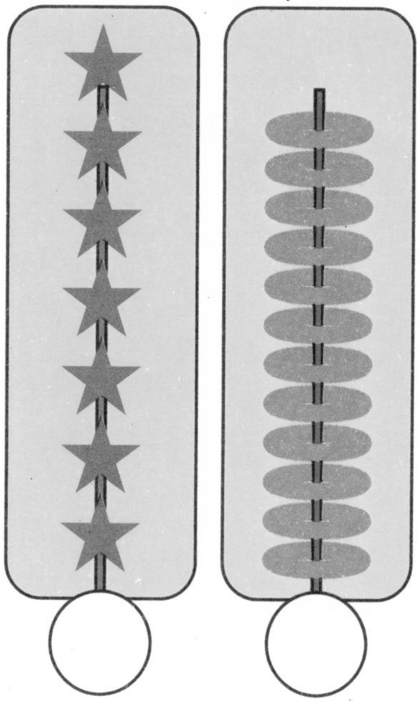

Find the answers.

14	+	4	=	
+		+		+
1	+	1	=	
=		=		=
	+		=	

Match the words with the numbers.

Eighth

Second

Ninth

Fifth

How many footballs?

Match the words to the correct picture.

Fourth

Fifth

Third

First

Second

Write in the missing numbers.

3

1

52

Colour second, fifth, eighth and eleventh giraffes.

Count and add the following.

      _____ + _____ = _____

Look at the picture and write the answers.

$1+2 = \boxed{}$ $5+1 = \boxed{}$

$3+1 = \boxed{}$ $2+3 = \boxed{}$

Encircle the number that is equal to the number of object in the circle.

Hop on and jump to find the answers.

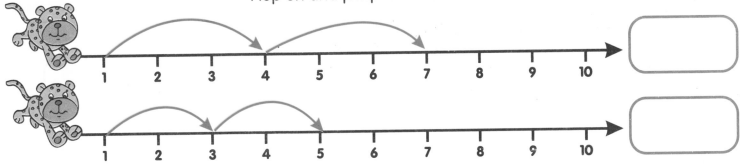

Write the numbers in the correct sequence.

	2	3		5		7	8		10
2			6	8	10			16	20

53

Encircle first, third and fifth pictures.

Count the flowers.

Colour the squirrels whose sums are same.

2+5   8+3   3+1
7+1   4+6   10+1

Look at the pictures and write the digits in the squares.

What comes after 9?

9 __

[ ] − [ ] = [ ]   [ ] − [ ] = [ ]

Write the answers correctly.

7-1 = [ ]

7-3 = [ ]

54

Multiply and colour the Ice creams as per the given codes.

10 = Red   20 = Yellow

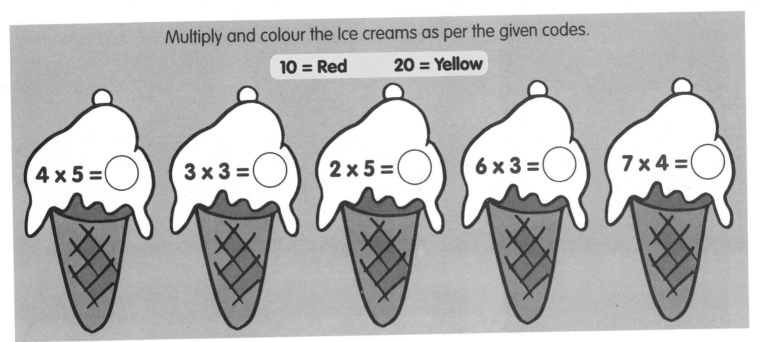

4 × 5 =   3 × 3 =   2 × 5 =   6 × 3 =   7 × 4 =

Draw a line to match the numbers.

⑦   ⑨

7	2
8	4
4	3
5	0

8	2
5	1
4	4
6	3

Help the monkey reach the banana with sum of nine.

6+3	8+4	3+6	8+8	7+8
5+4	4+4	3+2	8+7	3+7
3+6	8+1	3+6	3+1	5+5
4+5	7+2	1+8	5+4	3+6

How many stars can you see?

Put the correct signs + or -, in the circles to complete the sums.

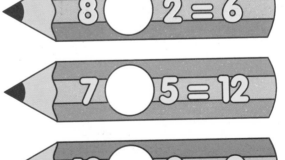

4 ◯ 4 = 8

8 ◯ 2 = 6

7 ◯ 5 = 12

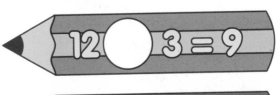

12 ◯ 3 = 9

5 ◯ 5 = 10

55

Find two aeroplanes with similar answers.

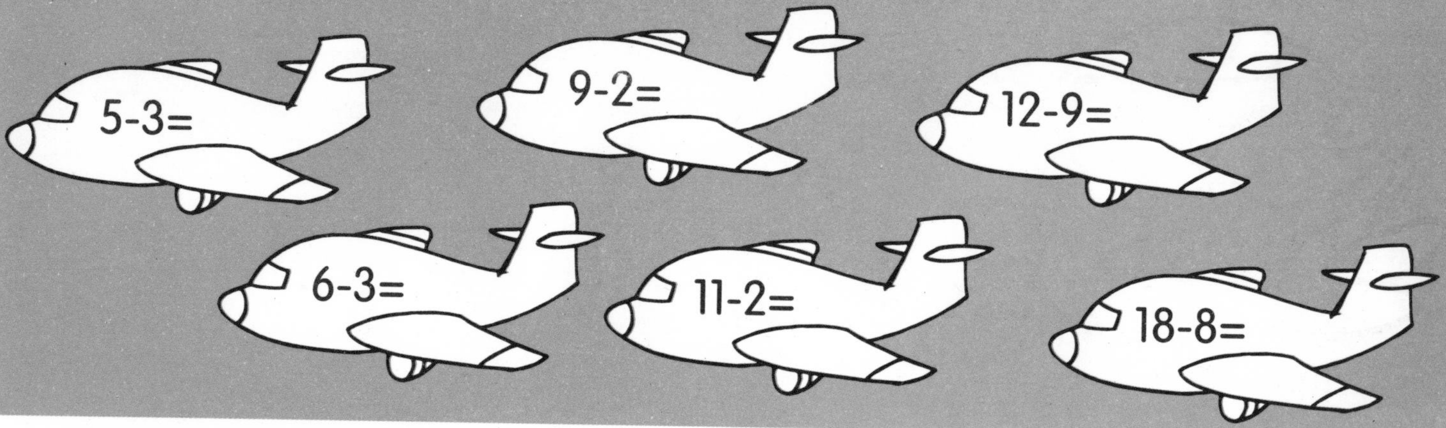

5-3=

9-2=

12-9=

6-3=

11-2=

18-8=

Find the total number of carrots and if 1 is taken away by the rabbit, how many are left?

Encircle the lowest number.

5   8   4   2   9

Encircle the honey bee whose answer comes to 55. BUZZZZZZZ!

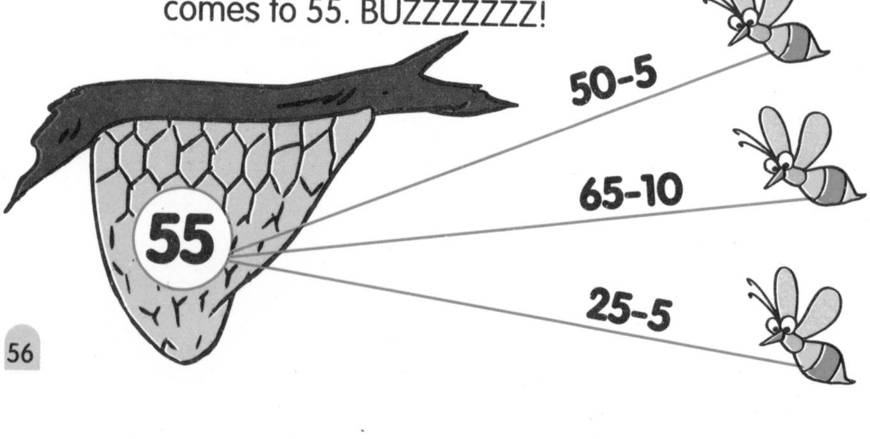

55

50-5

65-10

25-5

Match the boys with the correct answer caps.

30   50   40

40+10   15+5

20+10   10+6

40+40   35+15

Count and complete the blanks.

| | + | | + | | + | | + | |

5 Times 3 = ☐

Put the numbers accurately.

7	+	11	=	
+		+		+
9	+	13	=	
=		=		=
	+		=	40

Identify the jumbled pieces and place them in order.

1

Skip count to help the cub reach her mother.

10

8

☐   7

☐

☐

2   3

1

Find the total.

 = ○

 = ○

Complete the squares by adding 5 to each number.

15   +5   +5   +5   +5   +5   +5

Draw same number of smileys in all boxes.

Write the numbers from the greatest to the smallest.

25 10 15 3 5

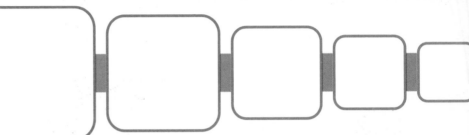

Look at the pictures to find the answers.

Write how many tens are there?

37 = _____ tens

55 = _____ tens

43 = _____ tens

59 = _____ tens

Colour the number that comes after the given number.

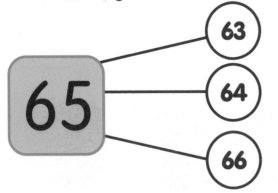

65

63

64

66

Sun = ◯   Ostrich = ◯   Eggs = ◯

Read the number names and write tens and ones.

Forty-six _____ tens _____ ones

Twenty-five _____ tens _____ ones

Encircle the 3s.

2 3 4 2
1 5
2 2 3
3 2 4
1 4 2 3 4 1
2 3 2 2
2 3 1 3
5 1 2 3 3
3 5 1 2

Encircle the correct number of kites.

13
14
12
17

Add up and write the answers.

Colour the odd numbers.

Colour the star as given.

★ 4
☆ ☆
☆ ☆
☆ ☆
☆ ☆

1 5 4
6 2 7
9 3
10
8

59

Match the pair of numbers to the numbered rabbits that come in between them.

24	26
34	36
44	46
36	38
10	12

Colour the greatest number.

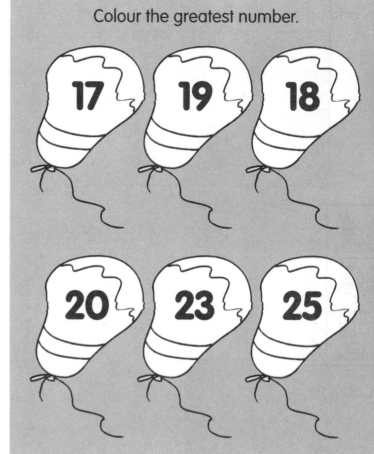

17 19 18

20 23 25

Rack your brain.

10	+	19	=	
+		+		+
12	+	9	=	
=		=		=
	+		=	

Colour the picture using the codes.

Even numbers =
Odd numbers =

Tick the correct answer.

20+10

25 ○
30 ○
35 ○
40 ○

Look at the animal codes and then add up the animals and birds together.

There are 12 fishes, 6 more fishes add to the group. Draw and complete the sum and write the count.

12 + __ = ☐

Count the different shapes separately.

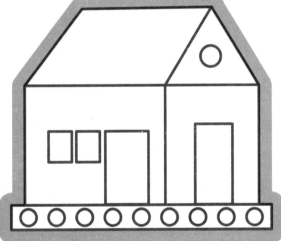

Total number of shapes

■ + ⬤ + ▲ = ☐

Fill up the missing number.

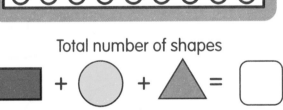

Find the answer.

8+4-9= ◯

Add 5 to the numbers on each joker, and then match the answers with the balls.

Write the number that is 2 less than the number on each book.

 **10**  **15**  **8**  **12**

_____   _____   _____   _____

Solve the following sums to get the answer shown in the circle.

25

5 × __   __ + 8

30 − __   6 + __

__ + 13

Count the tea cups and then solve the mathematical problem.

 − **5** = ☐

Follow the numbers that are multiples of 2 and help the dog find the bone.

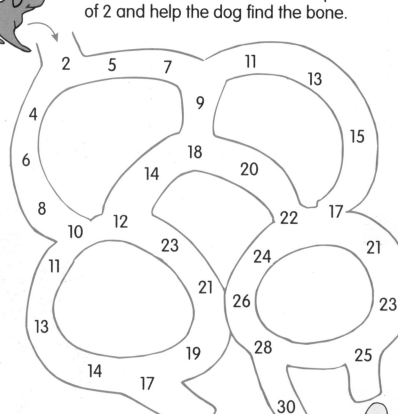

2   5   7   11   13
4   9   15
6   18   20
14
8   22   17
10   12   23   24   21
11   21   26   23
13   19   28   25
14   17   30

Crack the division sums. Then match the answers with the correct pictures.

15 ÷ 3 = ☐

14 ÷ 2 = ☐

24 ÷ 6 = ☐

32 ÷ 4 = ☐

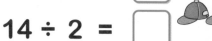

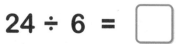

Solve the sums. Write the answers in the blank boxes.

book = 15 pizza = 7 jacket = 6

 −  = ☐

 +  = ☐

 +  = ☐

Match the number with the correct set.

5   2   3   4

Join the numbers correctly.

24
18   21   27 30
15
12
9
6
3

Add up the objects.

Draw a line to match similar numbers.

Colour the circles which have odd numbers.

1	2	3	4	5	6	7	8	9	10
11	12	13	14	15	16	17	18	19	20
21	22	23	24	25	26	27	28	29	30
31	32	33	34	35	36	37	38	39	40
41	42	43	44	45	46	47	48	49	50

63

Tick the number that equals to the number of objects in each set.

Set 1 (bags): (2) (3) (4)

Set 2 (ice creams): (5) (6) (7)

Set 3 (boys): (3) (4) (5)

Complete the number grid.

11	+	20	=	
+		+		+
8	+	6	=	
=		=		=
	+		=	

Use a mirror to solve maths problems.

[_____] = 6 + 3   [_____] = 14 - 5

Count and tick.

(12) (11) (13)

Fill up the missing numbers.

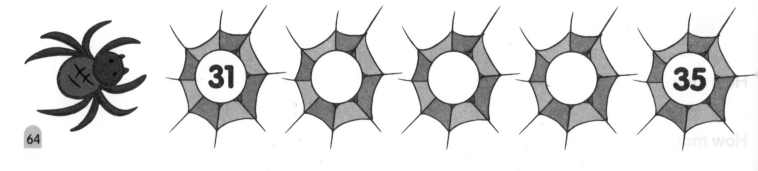

31 ( ) ( ) ( ) 35

Number the picture pieces in the correct order.

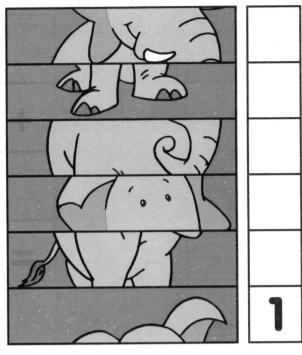

1

Count and write the number of feet.

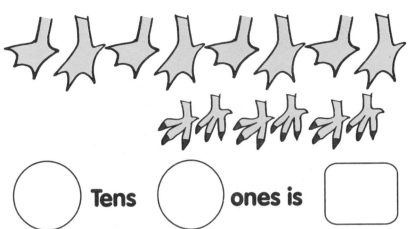

◯ **Tens** ◯ **ones is** ☐

Colour the boxes that show a
difference of 4 to find a path from
the hen to the egg.

2-1	5-3	7-2	8-1	9-3
8-4	7-3	6-1	9-8	7-6
3-2	6-4	6-2	5-2	7-5	6-3
7-5	8-6	5-1	9-5	

Count and write total number of dots.

Look at the pictures and answer.

SET A

SET B

How many pictures does set A have? _____

How many pictures does set B have? _____

Colour any two cats to make 12.

Calculate and tick the correct answer.

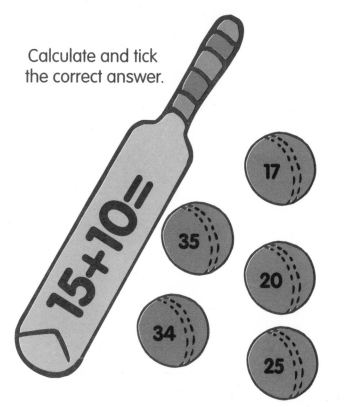

$15+10=$

17
35
20
34
25

Colour the sets that have the same number of pictures.

Count the number of objects.

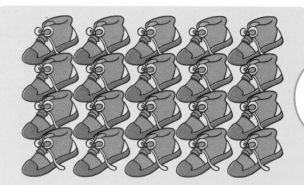

Add and find the answers.

Can you complete the maths grid?

9	+	15	=	
+		+		+
18	+	12	=	
=		=		=
	+		=	54

Snakes = ◯   Flowers = ◯   Clouds = ◯

Add 4 to the number and help the girl reach the last pizza.

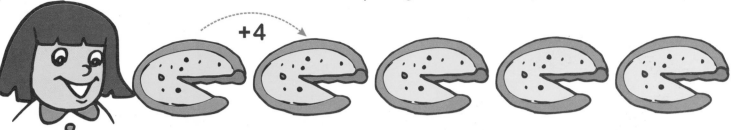

Take away 1 and write the correct answers.

10 - 1 = ___

18 - 1 = ___

20 - 1 = ___

Colour as many pictures as the number given in the centre.

Put the correct numbers to solve the addition sums.

__ + __ = 40

__ + __ = 40

__ + __ = 40

__ + __ = 35

__ + __ = 35

__ + __ = 35

How many feathers are flying in the sky? Tick the correct answer.

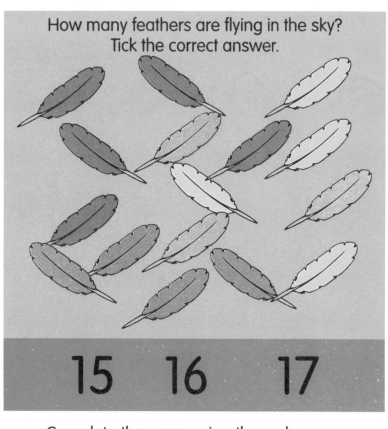

15   16   17

Complete the sums using the codes.

Book = 3   Starfish = 9   Shirt = 7

📘 + 👕 = ☐

⭐ − 📘 = ☐

👕 + ⭐ = ☐

📘 + ⭐ = ☐

Colour the box that give the answer in the circle.

45

15+15

20+35

40+5

25+30

If there are 4 butterflies and 1 flies away, how many are left?

_____

Tick the wrong counts in the table.

2	3
4	6
6	9
8	13
10	15
11	18
14	22
16	24
17	27
20	30

Write the missing numbers. .

7   21   35 →

Colour the box of the honey bee that lives in the hive.

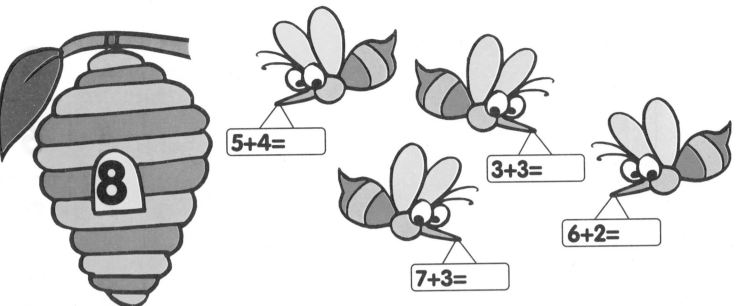

5+4=

3+3=

6+2=

7+3=

Count and add.

dogs

☐

+

dog

☐

=

dogs
altogether

☐

Solve the subtraction and
write answer in the circle.

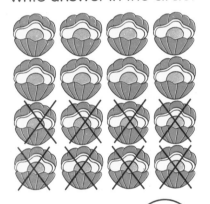

16-8 = ◯

Count the pencils and colour the
same number of circles.

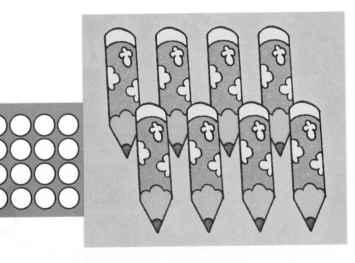

Add and find the answers.

Butterflies = ◯   Flowers = ◯

Sum up the numbers and write the answers.

10 + 20 = ☐

20 + 20 = ☐

30 + 20 = ☐

40 + 20 = ☐

50 + 20 = ☐

30 + 10 = ☐

40 + 10 = ☐

50 + 10 = ☐

60 + 10 = ☐

70 + 10 = ☐

Count and then cross out half of the pictures.

Half of ◯ is ◯

Half of ◯ is ◯

How many groups of 4 are there? Then write the total in the space given below.

Number of groups: ☐

Total deer: ☐

Find the answers quickly.

2	+	17	=	
+		+		+
17	+	7	=	
=		=		=
	+		=	**43**

The wizard has mixed up the spots of these animals. Can you draw the spots on their bodies equally?

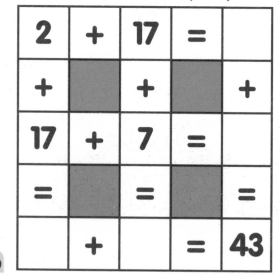

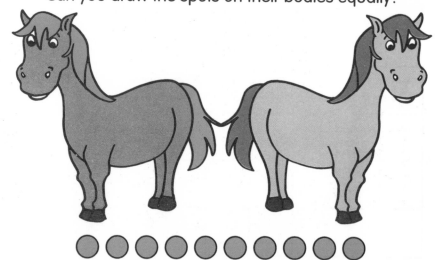

Count and colour the box with 6 pictures.

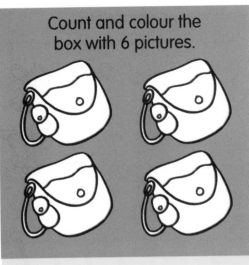

Count the objects and write the answer in the circles below.

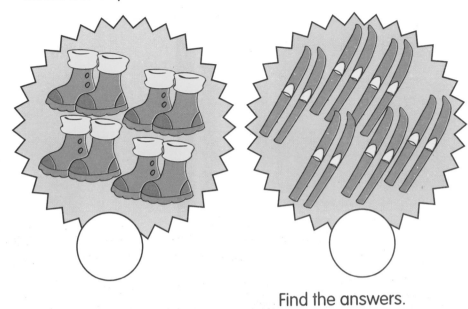

How many cups are there?

Find the answers.

$$8 - 7 =$$

$$9 \div 3 =$$

Find and write the missing numbers from 2-10.

Say aloud the numbers and learn to write them.

11	12	13	14	15	16	17	18	19	20
11	12	13	14	15	16	17	18	19	20

Colour the biggest number.

8   11   13

6   17

Count the number of owls sitting on the branches and encircle the number that shows the correct count.

6   7   8

Colour the fourth page.

Count the number of eggs.

In the basket

Out of the basket

Total eggs

Count the number of shapes in each box.

How many stars?
How many squares?

How many circles?
How many triangles?

72

Study each pattern and draw the missing figures.

(3) (6) (   ) (12) (   ) (18) (   ) (24) (27) (30)

(33) (36) (   ) (42) (45) (   ) (51) (54) (   ) (60)

Count and tick the correct number.

(19) (20) (21) (22)

Make the giraffe look complete.

5
10•
15 •
20•
•40
25 •
65   70
•60
45
30•   35   •   •55
50

How many groups of cherries are there? Find the total.

Groups = [   ]   **Total =** [   ]

Fill up the blanks. One has been done for you.

$2 + 2 + 2 + 2 =$ __2 X 4__ $=$ __8__

$3 + 3 + 3 + 3 =$ _____ $=$ ____

$4 + 4 + 4 + 4 =$ _____ $=$ ____

$5 + 5 + 5 + 5 =$ _____ $=$ ____

73

Multiply on the number lines.

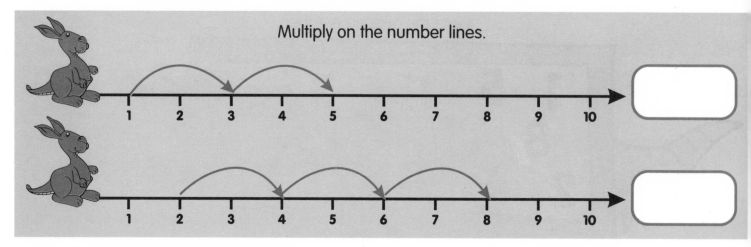

Solve the maths problems. Colour the pictures according to the given codes.

10, colour it Red	8, colour it Yellow	6, colour it Green

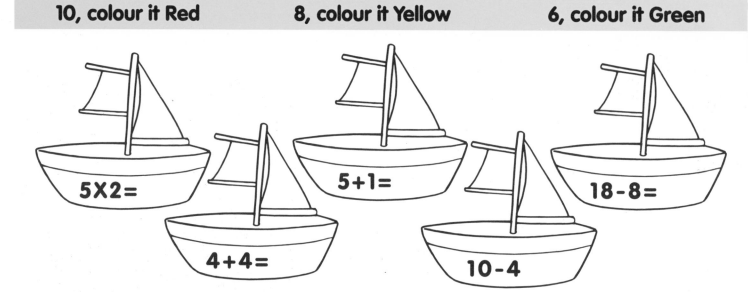

5X2=

4+4=

5+1=

10-4

18-8=

Match each pencil with its correct answer book.

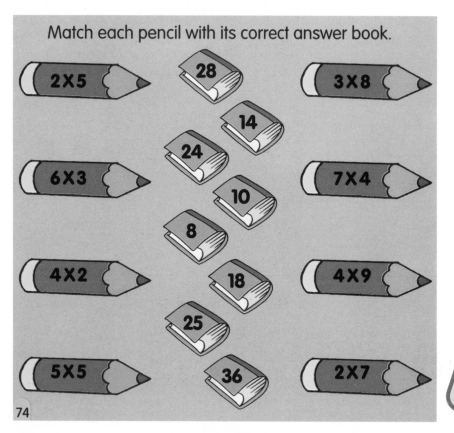

2X5

6X3

4X2

5X5

28

14

24

10

8

18

25

36

3X8

7X4

4X9

2X7

Multiply and find the answer.

X 7 =

Beside each dice, write the number that is one more than the number displayed on it.

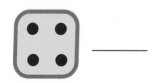

_____

_____   _____

Write the missing number.

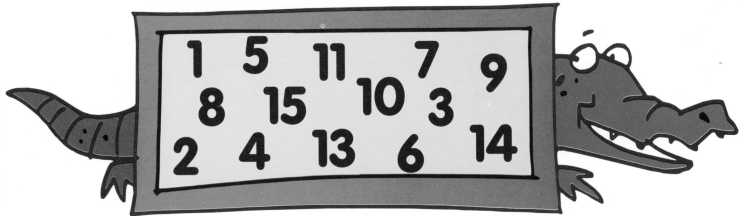

Decode and solve.

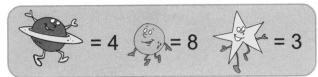

 = ◯

 = ◯

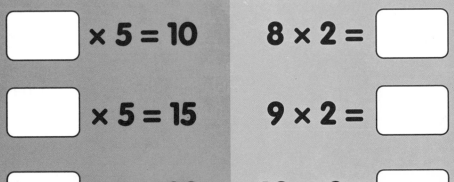 = ◯

Count the number of different types of fishes and write the answers in the circles.

Fill up the missing numbers.

☐ × 5 = 10	8 × 2 = ☐
☐ × 5 = 15	9 × 2 = ☐
☐ × 5 = 20	10 × 2 = ☐
☐ × 5 = 25	4 × 2 = ☐

Look at the picture and write the answer.

Up _____ **Down** _____

75

Match the following.

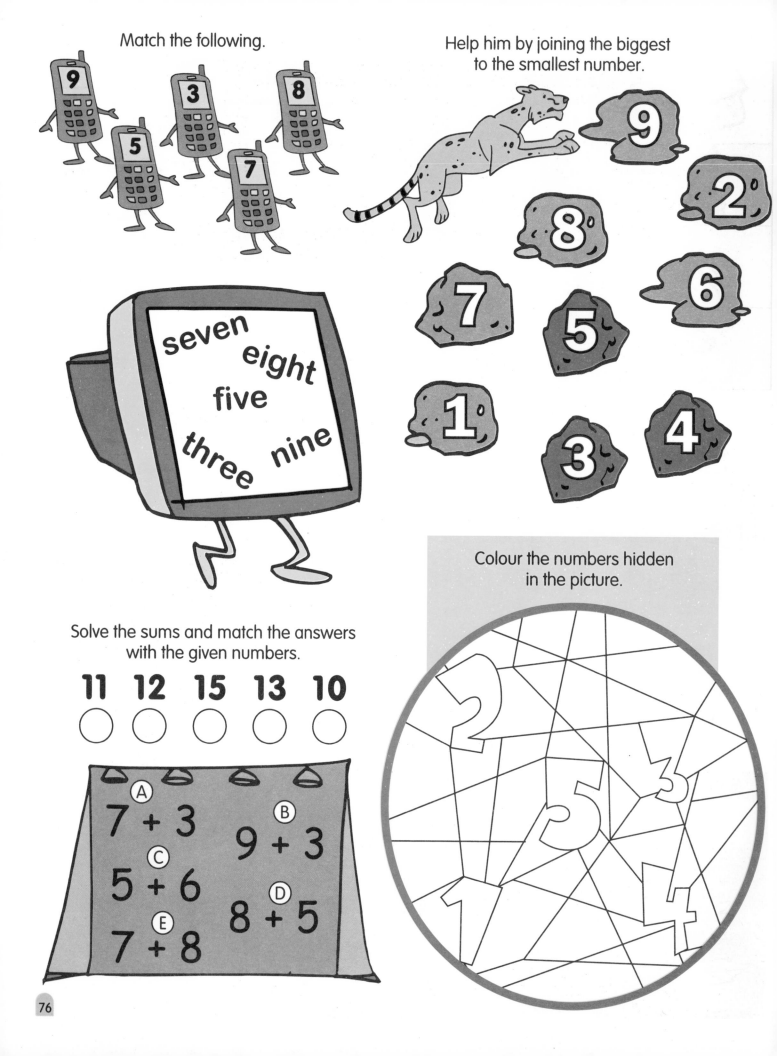

Help him by joining the biggest to the smallest number.

seven eight five three nine

9 3 8 5 7

9 2 8 7 6 5 1 3 4

Colour the numbers hidden in the picture.

Solve the sums and match the answers with the given numbers.

11   12   15   13   10
◯   ◯   ◯   ◯   ◯

A 7 + 3
B 9 + 3
C 5 + 6
D 8 + 5
E 7 + 8

Number the pictures in the correct order.

Solve the picture sum. Write the answer.

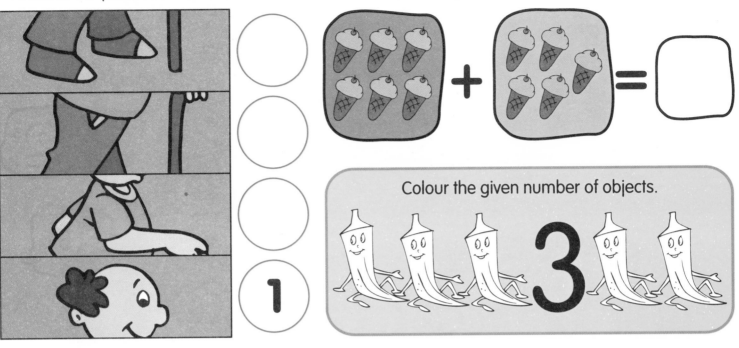

Colour the given number of objects.

3

How many bags are there?

7 6
9 8

Count and tick the number of flowers.

4   13   12   9   11

Count the ducks.

Encircle the odd numbers.

11 15 19
14 16
13 15 17
23 12

Colour the pictures in accordance with the shades shown.

1 ▭▭▭▶ 2 ▭▭▭▶ 3 ▭▭▭▶

Calculate and colour as per the answer.
Hint: If the answer is 4, colour four fishes.

22-19= ◯

Write the missing numbers 1-100.

1				5				9	
		13			16				
		23					28	29	
31			34					39	
	42					47			50
		53					58		
61				65					
			74					79	80
		83				87			
	92							99	

How many square and triangles
are there in the painting?

Multiply and find the answer by connecting
the boy with the respective drum.

Which of the following is correct?

4 × 6 = 30 ☐

5 × 6 = 30 ☐

Calculate and find the answers
of the questions.

Colour the question
yellow if its answer is 18 and shade
it red if its answer is 16.

18= Yellow   16= Red

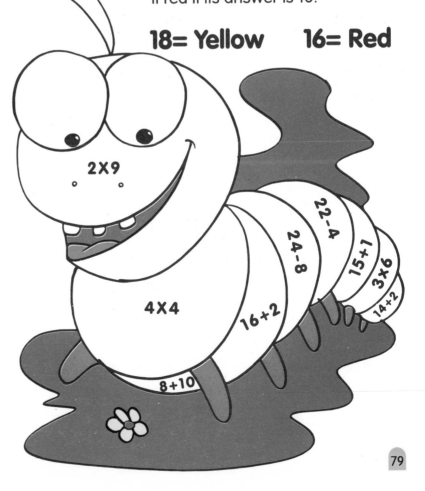

Add up and encircle the equal number.

5   6   7   8   9

9   10   11   12   13

Write the number missing from the table 5.

5, 35, 40, 45, 50, 20, 30, 10, 15

Fill up the missing numbers in each square.

4	+		=	7
-		-		-
	+	1	=	
=		=		=
3	+		=	5

Solve the sums.

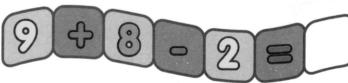

9 + 8 - 2 =

Count the coins and write on the piggy bank.

Write the missing numbers.

( ) (13) ( )

(11) (15)

( ) ( )

(19)

(16) ( )

Help the boy solve the maths puzzle.

10	+	2	=	
+		+		+
6	+	10	=	
=		=		=
	+		=	28

Cross out 5 spoons from the set and find the total.

Colour the odd numbered aeroplanes.

1   2   3   4   5   6

Solve the addition problem.

15 + 12 =

Write the missing numbers and reach the fish.

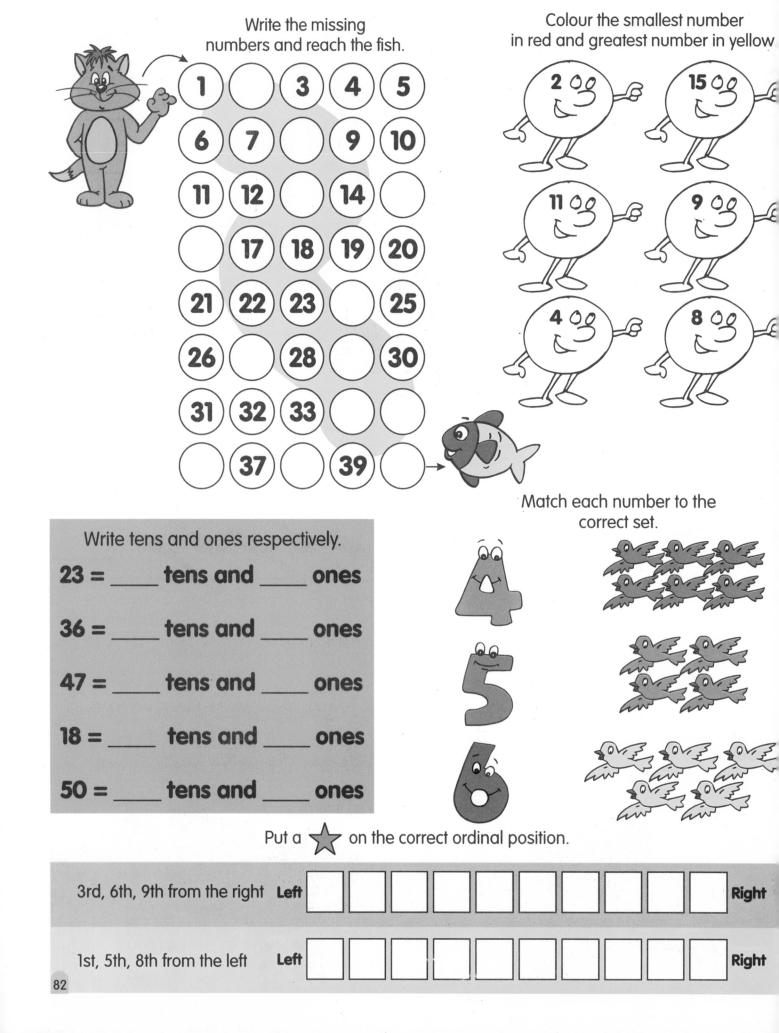

1	◯	3	4	5
6	7	◯	9	10
11	12	◯	14	◯
◯	17	18	19	20
21	22	23	◯	25
26	◯	28	◯	30
31	32	33	◯	◯
◯	37	◯	39	◯

Colour the smallest number in red and greatest number in yellow

2   15

11   9

4   8

Write tens and ones respectively.

23 = _____ tens and _____ ones

36 = _____ tens and _____ ones

47 = _____ tens and _____ ones

18 = _____ tens and _____ ones

50 = _____ tens and _____ ones

Match each number to the correct set.

4

5

6

Put a ⭐ on the correct ordinal position.

| 3rd, 6th, 9th from the right | **Left** | | | | | | | | | | | **Right** |

| 1st, 5th, 8th from the left | **Left** | | | | | | | | | | | **Right** |

82

Follow the number patterns and fill up the missing numbers.

33   34   ⬜   ⬜   ⬜   38

Fill up the answers in the circles.

$19 + 8 - 5 = \bigcirc$

$22 + 7 - 3 = \bigcirc$

Colour the questions that have the answers as shown in the red and blue circles.

15-5	14-8		5 X 8	15-7
35-10	**35** 25+10		45-8	**40** 35+6
23+10	10-8		10+35	12+24

Solve the subtraction problems.

```
  3 3          2 7
- 2 2        - 1 3
_____        _____


  3 5          2 3
- 2 3        - 1 1
_____        _____
```

Put the pictures in the order 1 to 4.

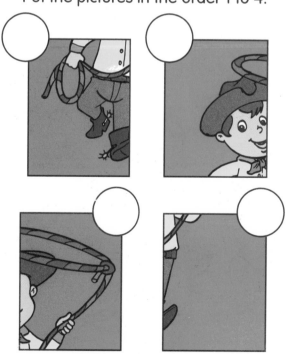

83

Count the pieces of cheese and write the correct number in the box given below.

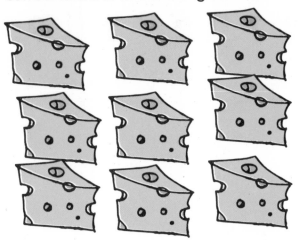

I found ☐ cheese

Colour any three leaves to make number 15.

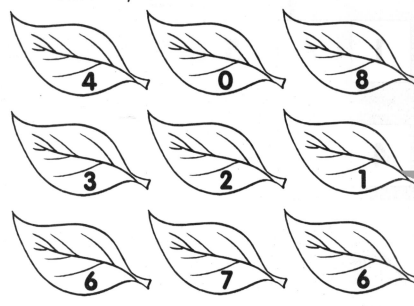

Take away 2 and write the correct answers.

$8 - 2 =$ ◯

$5 - 2 =$ ◯

Colour as many birds as the number given.

3

Can you write the answers accurately?

8	+	9	=	
+		+		+
3	+	6	=	
=		=		=
	+		=	26

Colour the number 2s.

| 1 | 4 | 5 | 2 | 3 | 2 | 7 | 2 | 2 | 9 |

Colour the number 3s.

| 4 | 3 | 8 | 3 | 2 | 3 | 5 | 3 | 7 | 6 |

Tick the sets that have the same number of pictures.

Match the pictures with the correct answers.

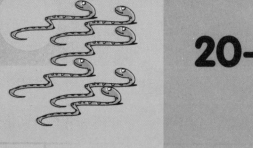

20-17

25-21

30-24

Encircle the hidden numbers and write the missing ones.

Use a mirror to solve these puzzles.

12 - 5 =

4 + 3 =

4 X 3 =

85

Count, subtract and write the answer.

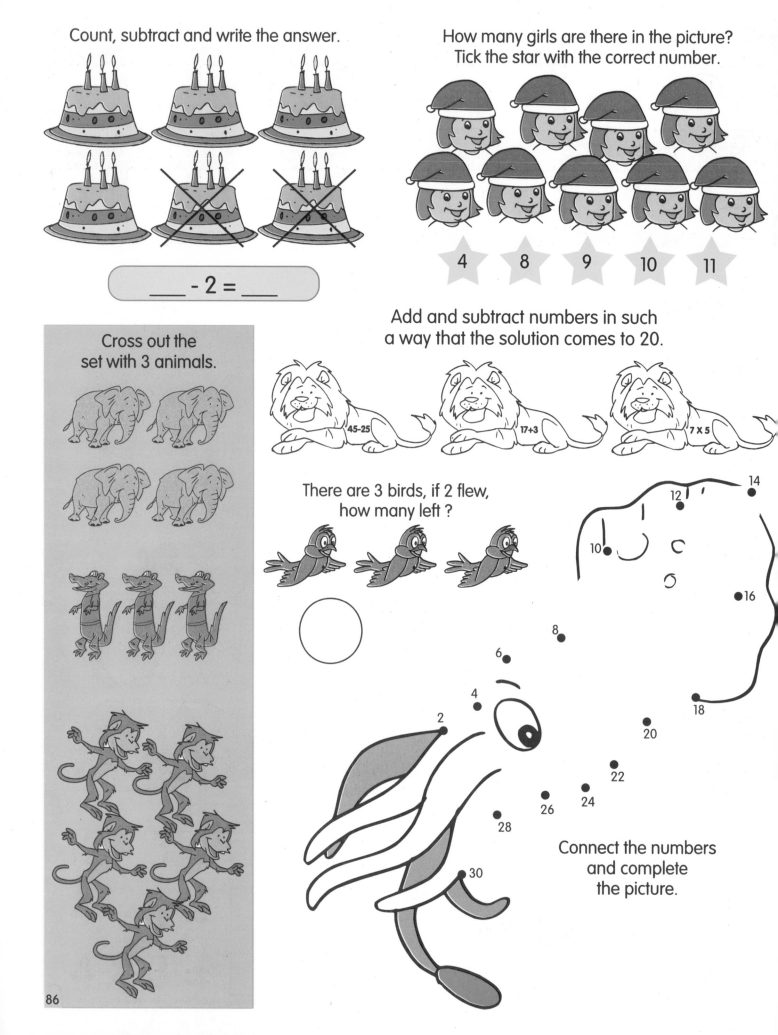

___ - 2 = ___

How many girls are there in the picture?
Tick the star with the correct number.

4   8   9   10   11

Cross out the
set with 3 animals.

Add and subtract numbers in such
a way that the solution comes to 20.

45-25   17+3   7 X 5

There are 3 birds, if 2 flew,
how many left ?

Connect the numbers
and complete
the picture.

86

Count the number of balls of wool.

Cross out the extra sun so that the set matches with the number given.

7

Solve the problems.

$\_\_\_ - 2 = 3$

$4 - \_\_\_ = 1$

Solve the sums.

Find the total.

Colour the boxes that show a difference of 6 to find a path from the cat to the fish.

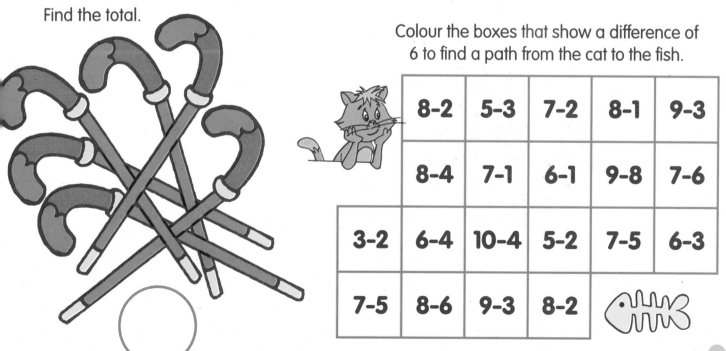

8-2	5-3	7-2	8-1	9-3
8-4	7-1	6-1	9-8	7-6
3-2	6-4	10-4	5-2	7-5	6-3
7-5	8-6	9-3	8-2	

Write the numbers that add up to give the sum shown in the big circles.

10   5   ( )

20   5   ( )

30   5   ( )

Write the missing number.

71   73

How do you make 12? Fill up the gap to make 12.

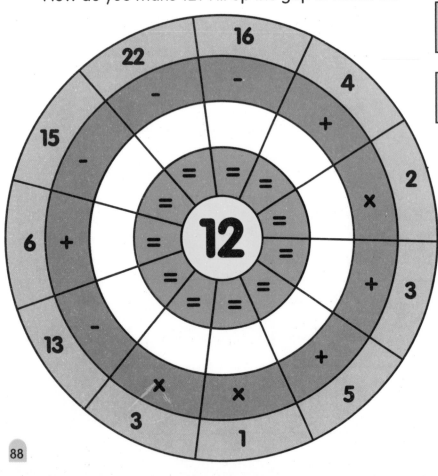

Write the numbers that come after.

0	1	
8	9	
2	3	
5	6	
3	4	

4
5
1
8
10
2
7

Determine the answers.

6	+		=	11
+		+		+
	+	8	=	
=		=		=
8	+		=	21

In each set, count the number of objects and write its total and half.

___altogether.
Half is ___.

___altogether.
Half is ___.

___altogether.
Half is ___.

Help the octopus trace his way to the coral reef.

Tick the bird with biggest number.

 3
 9

 7
 4

8
6

1
1

Write the number that comes between the given numbers.

 42 ___ 44

 75 ___ 77

Colour any 2 balloons so that they add to the numbers written in the circles.

12

8
3
4

18

9
9
7

Look at the pictures and fill up the blanks.

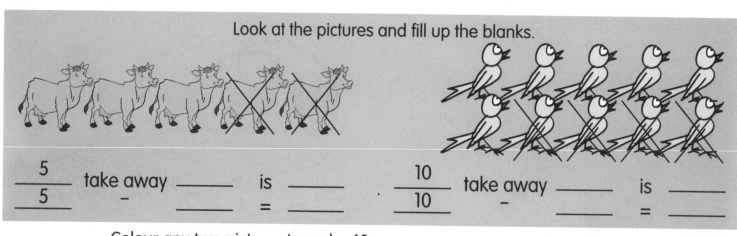

$\dfrac{5}{5}$ take away _____ is _____

— _____

= _____

$\dfrac{10}{10}$ take away _____ is _____

— _____

= _____

Colour any two pictures to make 40.

30+10   18+3   20+10   20+20

Count the total number of giraffes and tick the appropriate number.

6   7   8   9

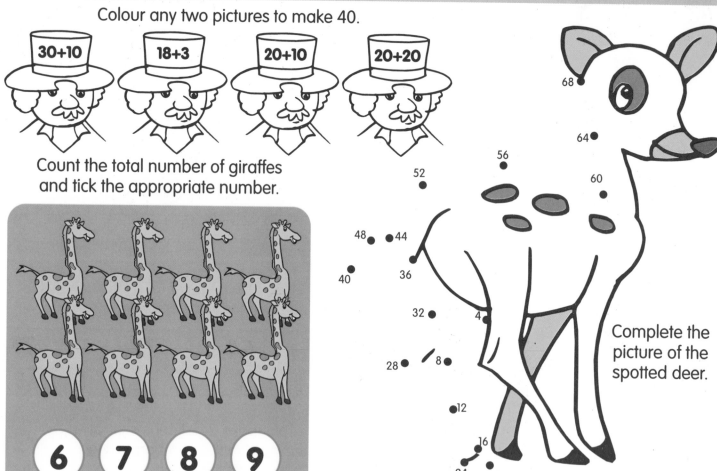

Complete the picture of the spotted deer.

Solve the sums and then connect them by drawing a line to their respective answers.

24   16   17   20   22

15+2   14+8   17+3   11+5   18+6

Write the numbers in ascending order.

Crack the maths grid.

	+	5	=	6
+		+		+
7	+		=	
=		=		=
	+		=	20

Tick the correct number.

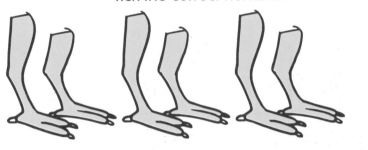

5
6
7

Write the number that comes between the given numbers.

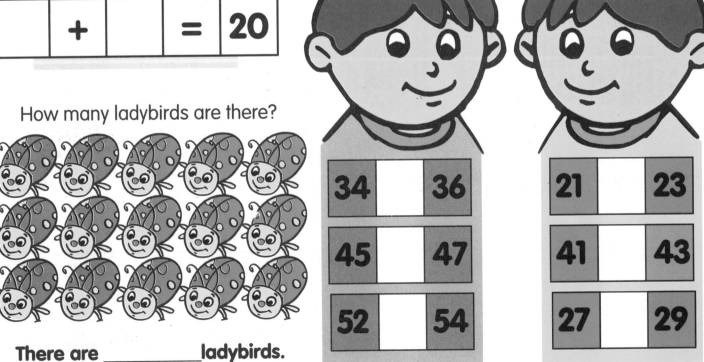

34		36
45		47
52		54

21		23
41		43
27		29

How many ladybirds are there?

There are _____ ladybirds.

Find the answers and match them with the correct pictures.

$3 \times 3 =$ ___

$2 \times 3 =$ ___

$4 \times 3 =$ ___

Find the answers.

$$\begin{array}{r} 30 \\ +34 \\ \hline \end{array}$$

$$\begin{array}{r} 40 \\ +22 \\ \hline \end{array}$$

$$\begin{array}{r} 55 \\ +34 \\ \hline \end{array}$$

$$\begin{array}{r} 48 \\ +27 \\ \hline \end{array}$$

Calculate the maths problem.

$16 + 8 - 4 = \boxed{}$

Colour the even numbers.

Look at the pictures
and fill up the circles.

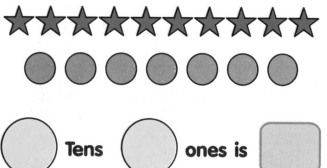

◯ Tens   ◯ ones is   ▭

92

Colour the numbers using the hints given.

8 = ⬤   0 = ⬤   7 = ⬤   9 = ⬤

Look at the numbers and fill up the blanks.

| 1 | 2 | 3 | 4 | 5 | 6 | 7 | 8 | 9 | 10 |

Which number :

a. comes before 7? _____

b. come after 3? _____

Count the birds flying in the sky?

Count the pictures and tick the correct numbers.

3   4   5

8   6   7

Colour the number 8s.

| 8 | 2 | 3 | 5 | 8 | 8 | 1 | 8 | 1 | 8 |

Colour the number 5s.

| 4 | 5 | 3 | 5 | 4 | 5 | 5 | 7 | 6 | 5 |

Sum up the books and write.

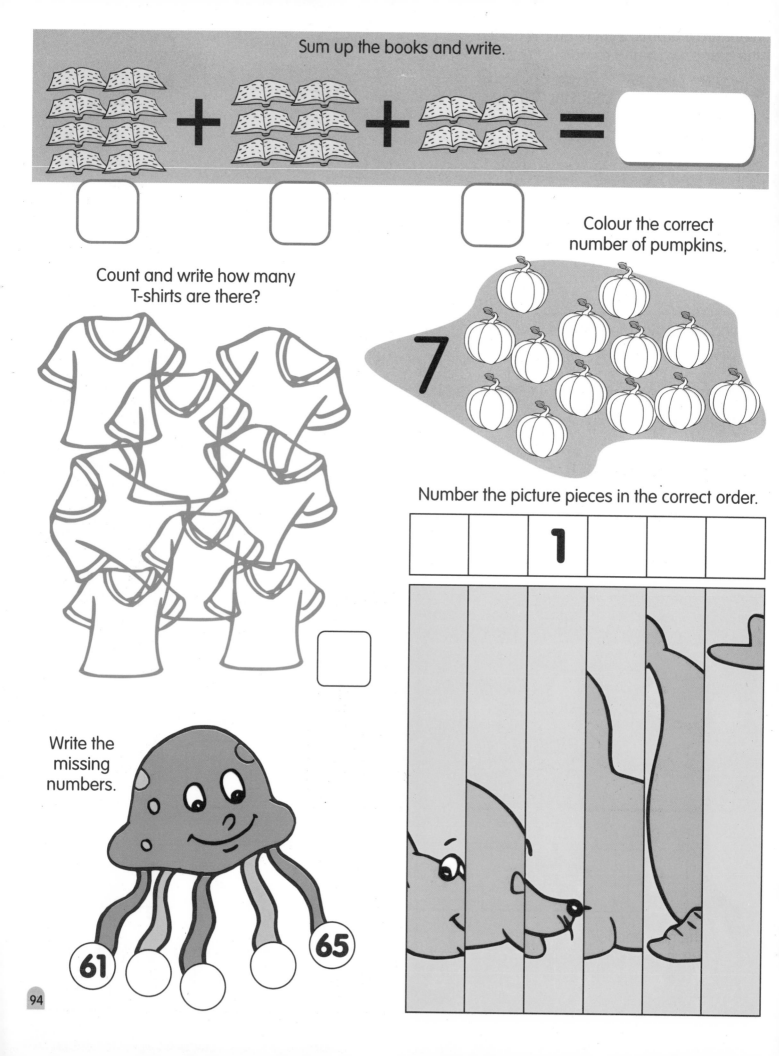

+ **+** **=** [ ]

[ ] [ ] [ ]

Colour the correct number of pumpkins.

7

Count and write how many T-shirts are there?

[ ]

Number the picture pieces in the correct order.

		1			

Write the missing numbers.

61 ( ) ( ) ( ) 65

There are 8 drums, 2 more drums added the group. Draw and complete the sum.

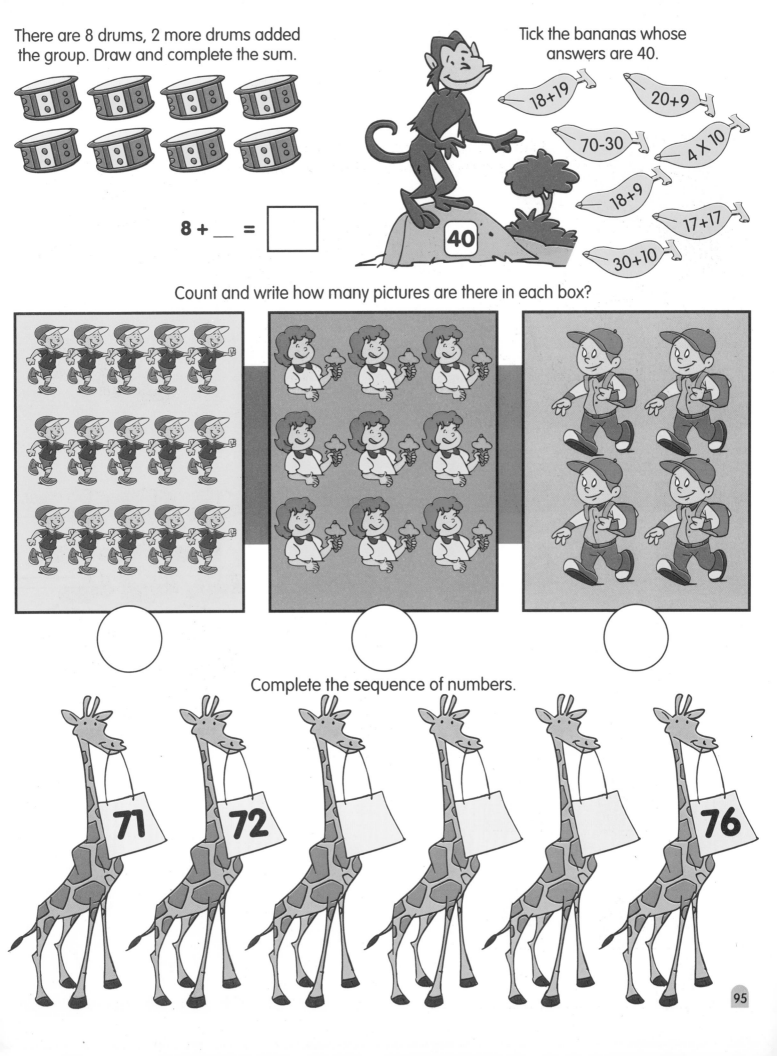

8 + __ = ☐

Tick the bananas whose answers are 40.

18+19

20+9

70-30

4 X 10

18+9

17+17

30+10

40

Count and write how many pictures are there in each box?

○   ○   ○

Complete the sequence of numbers.

71   72   __   __   __   76

95

There is a pattern in this row of numbers. Can you find the missing numbers?

8, 16, ___, 32, ___, 48, ___, 64.

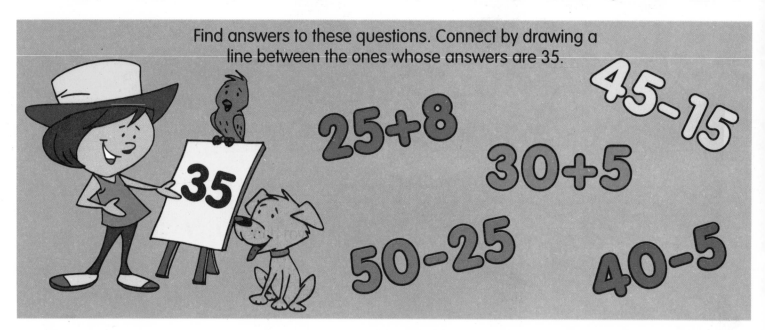

Find answers to these questions. Connect by drawing a line between the ones whose answers are 35.

25+8

45-15

30+5

50-25

40-5

Put the numbers that come before and after.

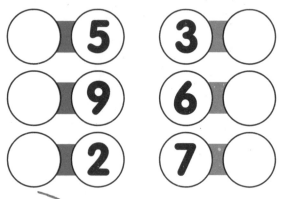

Solve the subtraction problem and write in the box.

18-7 =

Fill up the correct figures in the squares.

	+	8	=	14
+		+		+
7	+		=	9
=		=		=
13	+		=	

Colour the circles that have smallest number.